BOWERBIRDS
NATURE, ART & HISTORY

FRITH&FRITH

BOWERBIRDS

NATURE, ART & HISTORY

Clifford B. Frith & Dawn W. Frith

Photography by Clifford B. Frith

FRITH&FRITH

Dedicated
to the memory of
Norman Wettenhall
1915-2000

The authors gratefully acknowledge the help of the
Norman Wettenhall Foundation in the production of this work.

First published in Australia 2008 by Frith & Frith, P.O. Box 581, Malanda, Queensland, 4885
Copyright © in text and photographs: Clifford B. Frith & Dawn W. Frith (07) 40968105
except where otherwise credited and is the copyright of other photographers.

Designed by Clifford B. Frith & Dawn W. Frith. Copyright © Frith & Frith.

National Library of Australia Cataloguing-in-Publication Data:

Frith, Clifford B.
Bowerbirds : nature, art & history.

ISBN 97818764 3631.

Printed in China by Everbest.

1. Bowerbirds - Australia. I. Frith, Dawn W. II. Title.

598.8

Endpapers: A Vogelkop Bowerbird's bower, Arfak Mountains, Papua. By and courtesy of Nancy Woodman.
Half-title page: A Fawn-breasted Bowerbird on his bower with building material, Iron Range, Australia.
Frontispiece: Masked Bowerbirds; from John Gould's *The Birds of New Guinea and the adjacent Papuan Islands*.
Title page: First illustration of a Vogelkop Bowerbird's bower; from Otto Beccari 1877 (see Further reading).
Page 5, opposite: An immature male Satin Bowerbird at the bower of an adult male, Lamington, Queensland, Australia.
Page 6: An adult male Regent Bowerbird displays to an immature male, Lamington, Queensland, Australia.
Page 8: An adult male Flame Bowerbird, captive in Qatar.
Page 9: An adult male Fawn-breasted Bowerbird on his bower, Iron Range, Queensland, Australia.

FRITH&FRITH

CONTENTS

PROLOGUE

On the previous two pages, 10-11: A typical twin-towered Golden Bowerbird bower, the adult male adding a decoration to it, Paluma Range, north Queensland.

I can clearly recall when the bowerbirds first intrigued me. As an eleven year old, one of ten siblings of hard working parents, I attended a rough and tumble south London boys' high school, long since torn down. On my first day, at the school assembly, the kindly headmaster informed the ragtag gathering that the head boy, having been attacked by a mob of the school's 'students' on the last day of the previous term, was recovering well from several broken limbs and would return to school soon!

It was not long before I found refuge in the school 'library', a small and cluttered corner classroom full of tatty books. Here I spent as much time as possible reading about and enjoying the natural world. It was an escape from my life in the congested suburbs of south London. My life dramatically changed when I pulled a large format book from the stacks titled *The Wonders of Life on Earth* published by Life Inc. of New York in 1960. This book was a revelation to me. It depicted the wildlife of the Galapagos Islands and other such tropical and exotic places. It contained many fold-out pages that produced large features of magnificent composite artworks. Two of these features showed various bowerbirds displaying at their bowers. The text described the intrepid exploration of the remote New Guinea highland forests and grasslands by curator of birds at the American Museum of Natural History Dr. E. Thomas Gilliard. He studied bowerbird and bird of paradise behaviour there. It also informed me of Charles Darwin and how his voyage and work resulted in his theory of evolution by natural selection. This material profoundly moved and excited me, and I determined to become an ornithologist and to one day study the bowerbirds and birds of paradise. I was puzzled by just exactly how on earth the pressures of natural and sexual selection could have brought about these glorious and intriguing birds and their complex behaviour.

In 1965 my parents emigrated to Sydney, Australia, taking my three younger siblings and myself. The timing of this was unfortunate as I was then fifteen and found it necessary to leave school shortly after arriving in Australia, lacking any qualifications and subsequently unable to return to formal education. I was, however, at last able to see living bowerbirds in the wild. But my parents returned to England after only two years and, as a 17 year old, I had to go with them. There my enthusiasm and persistence found me a position in the Bird Department of the British Museum (Natural History) in London. My main qualification was my recently gained knowledge of Australian birds. The museum was, most fortuitously, preparing for a ten-month ornithological expedition to tropical Australia in 1968. During that expedition I observed many Western and Great Bowerbirds. By simply lying down beside a bower of the latter species I managed to take photographs of a male decorating his bower. The determination of this bird to attend his bower, even in the close presence of so strange an animal as myself, greatly impressed and fascinated me.

PROLOGUE

Back in London in 1969 I was thrilled to find the newly-published book *Birds of Paradise and Bower Birds* by my childhood hero E. Thomas Gilliard. This work summarised and synthesised Gilliard's impressive life work on these birds in New Guinea, and became my constant source of fascination and wonder. Sadly Gilliard died in 1967, aged 52, before his book was published.

In 1971 I learnt that the Royal Society of London was looking for someone to live a year on the remote tropical Indian Ocean island of Aldabra, with five other scientists, to study birds. I won the position and my life profoundly changed a second time - for there I met Dawn, an only child, who had already been on the atoll for eight months studying insects although with a Bachelor of Science degree in zoology and a doctorate in marine biology. We quickly realised that we shared a deep and abiding passion for wild things and places. Inevitably we came to talk of spending a shared future enjoying and studying animals in their natural tropical environments. For the first time I was able to fully share my long-term dream of working with living bowerbirds and birds of paradise in the forests of Australia and New Guinea with someone who could be as passionate about them as I was. This dream was not, however, to be realised for another half a decade.

Dawn left the atoll four months later and I languished there, although most fortunately able to busy myself in studying some wonderful birds peculiar to the island. Eight months later I joined Dawn in England and together we wrote up the results of the various zoological researches we had undertaken on Aldabra. A year later we travelled to Phuket Island in southern Thailand, where Dawn worked for the Danish Government as a senior marine biologist. There we studied mangrove ecology, hornbills and other birds, snakes, amphibians, fiddler crabs, and more, for four years. Dawn then not only readily agreed to my pursuing my lifelong dream of studying bowerbirds in Australia but also fully embraced ornithology as her own future field of zoological investigation.

Clifford Frith's first bowerbird photograph, taken when he was 18 years old, of a male Great Bowerbird arriving at his bower, Mt. Bell, Western Australia in June 1968.

A typical Golden Bowerbird's bower, with Dawn Frith beyond, Paluma Range, north Queensland.

We had read of a small mountaintop village called Paluma, 85 kilometres north of Townsville, in northern Queensland. There one could look down, from 900 metres above sea level, upon the Coral Sea and the Palm Island group from within rainforest in which four species of bowerbird and one species of bird of paradise lived. Paradise on earth to us! We purchased a Landrover and a large caravan in Sydney and drove the 2,000 kilometres north to Paluma where we spent the next 13 years studying bowerbirds. For the first three years we worked intensely, most daylight hours of every day.

One of the four bowerbirds that we studied was the Golden Bowerbird. At that time it was seen as the Holy Grail of the ten different bowerbirds in Australia. This was because of its remote and romantic tiny north Queensland mountaintop distribution and the vast stick bowers that the gloriously yellow-plumaged, long-tailed, adult males build. While bowers are typically twin towers built on the ground exceptional ones can be single or twin towered ones built entirely above ground. The bird itself is merely the size and weight of a Common or European Starling. At that time next to nothing was known about Golden Bowerbirds. The other three species we studied were the Black-eared Catbird, Tooth-billed Bowerbird and, to much less extent, the Satin Bowerbird. During those Paluma-based years we also made observations from hides on Spotted and Great Bowerbirds in the Charters Towers area of Queensland and Macgregor's, Archbold's, Fawn-breasted and Lauterbach's Bowerbirds in Papua New Guinea.

The basis of our studies was the netting and colour banding of the birds, so that we could then observe what went on between known individuals at bowers, nests, and elsewhere. Our study area was 50 hectares of rainforest that we had marked out into precise squares. In order to leg-band and retrap enough individuals we continued this systematic work over many years. This involved erecting numbers of nine and 12 metre lengths of bird netting between two vertical poles. So fine are these nets, that they are known as mist-nets. These nets have several strong fine lines of cord woven horizontally along their length a foot or so apart. As a flying bird hits the all-but invisible net its forward momentum and weight drops it below a horizontal cord line to become suspended in a long pocket of netting. Birds grasp the net mesh with their feet and were thus held firmly and safely until we removed them. We then quickly weighed and measured them and placed bands on their legs or noted details of pre-existing bands. These small coloured plastic bands together with a numbered alloy one do not bother the birds and many of them wore their bands for more than 20 years. This provided us with much information about their movements and interactions.

Dawn Frith at an arboreal single-towered bower of the Golden Bowerbird, Paluma Range, north Queensland.

To study the intimate lives of our banded birds we spent thousands of hours, usually six hours at each sitting (0600-1200 and 1200-1800 hours), watching their activities at bowers and at nests. This we did from within canvas hides, or blinds, armed with binoculars, stopwatch, pen and notebook. These were intensely exciting and scientifically richly rewarding times, as we were acutely aware of being the first ornithologists to learn much of the private lives of these most intriguing of birds. Sitting for hours in a hide deep within a tropical rainforest often provided memorable experiences. The morning chorus of bird song, dominated by that of the ground-frequenting Chowchilla, never failed to thrill us. Various birds busy with their own lives constantly provided interest as they walked, flew, and foraged right up to the hide, sometimes perching on it, oblivious of their audience. A Cassowary might stride up to our hide to peer inquisitively into one of the small observation 'windows'. Delightful pademelons, little kangaroos of the rainforest, wandered by, as did various smaller mammals and reptiles. There were dull moments, and indeed hours, when little happened but when it did these were more than made up for.

It was to be years into our studies before we made one particularly exciting and informative discovery. This observation brought about a full appreciation of the complex courtship display of the Golden Bowerbird. Moreover this understanding shed more light upon the courtship of closely related species in New Guinea and thus had broader significance within the bowerbird family.

We had been silently watching the bulky two metre high twin-towered stick bower of adult male Golden Bowerbird we knew as Red-over-white by his colour band combination. Interconnecting the two towers of his bower was his perch, about half a metre above the ground. At each end of this perch the sticks of the towers were far more meticulously placed and aligned to form two neat 'platforms' that contrasted conspicuously with the dishevelled accumulation of sticks forming the rest of the structure. Red-over-white had been busily coming and going to feed and to collect decorations for his bower since sunrise. In returning to his bower perch he often brought a bunch of pale green beard lichen, the pale whitish seedpods of a shrub, the creamy flowers of a rainforest tree, or the white flower of a jasmine vine or an orchid in his beak. These he added, with great care and attention, to the numerous bower decorations he had previously placed upon the 'platforms'. He would then sometimes fly but a metre or two away to cling to an adjacent sapling trunk in order to peer back at his bower in order to carefully assess the visual impact of his newly added decoration. If not to his complete satisfaction he would fly back to his bower, readjusts his decoration display, and then back to a sapling to again cast his eye over it until content with the result.

Red-over-white perched above his bower to give long loud rattling calls. These calls announce the location of his bower to females, as well as to rival males, of his kind. He surprised and delighted us by occasionally also producing mimicry of the calls of other kinds of birds, and of frogs and insects, that share his forest. This mimicry was so perfect in quality that we initially looked about for, for example, the Grey-headed Robin we thought we heard calling. Now and then Red-over-white replied to the calls of other bird species, once impressively answering the raucous screech of a Sulphur-crested Cockatoo calling overhead with his perfect imitation. It must have surprised the cockatoo even more than it did us.

Having perched near his bower for a while Red-over-white suddenly flew

Clifford Frith at an arboreal twin-towered Golden Bowerbird's bower, Paluma Range, north Queensland.

A tower and hide at a Spotted Bowerbird's nest, Charters Towers, Queensland.

purposefully to a knot hole in a nearby tree and took out from its depths a bunch of bright red wild pepper fruits. He ate several of them and then replaced the remainder into the tree hole. At that first instance we could hardly believe what we had seen, but many subsequent observations conclusively proved that male Golden Bowerbirds perform the rare behaviour of food caching. They store fruits in concealed sites immediately about their bowers for later consumption.

    We suddenly became aware of a conspicuous change in Red-over-white's demeanour, he sleeked his plumage tightly to his body and peered intensely in one direction into the forest. In the blink of an eye a second adult male appeared on Red-over-white's bower perch and the intruding rival was about to steal a beakfull of bower decorations to take to his own bower several hundred metres away. Red-over-white reacted just quickly enough, however, and, launching himself at his bower, he flew directly at his rival giving a loud agitated rattle call. The empty handed (or beaked!) intruder fled into the forest with Red-over-white in hot pursuit. But he must not press his eviction chase for too long, for there is always the possibility of another rival getting to his bower decorations in his absence! In this the caching of food about his bower is a real advantage, because it means that he has to leave his bower less often to find food.

    Later we again see Red-over-white suddenly change his demeanour. This time he started to call volubly, giving both rattle calls and a repertoire of mimicry delivered in an excited way. He performs a deep bow, then lowers his beak and repeatedly nods his head in a rapid and mechanical fashion. Female Red-over-green appears in the vegetation close to his bower. Red-over-white takes off from his perch to perform an extensive flight display over and about his vast bower. His wings beat slowly but extensively and thus highlight their brilliant yellow colour. Now and then he hovers before a slim sapling trunk, his bill tip all but touching it, as he flutters his wings while repeatedly and rapidly fanning and closing his brilliant yellow tail. As his central dark olive green pair of tail feathers conceals the yellow outer feathers each time his tail is closed this action causes a rapidly repeated flashing of brilliant yellow in the dense undergrowth. This aerial dance was wonderful for us to watch from such close proximity.

    Suddenly nervous female Red-over-green plucks up the courage to land on the bower perch. She closely scrutinises the quantity and quality of Red-over-white's bower decorations. Just as suddenly he quits his flight display and, to our great surprise, flies directly away from his bower to the far side of a nearby large tree trunk. His behaviour, in peering around the tree trunk in order to watch the female on his bower, is distinctly that of hiding himself from her view. From his hidden position he then 'whispers' a constant stream of perfect mimicry of the songs of numerous other birds, and of other sounds of his habitat, as a subsong that the female can presumably only just hear. As he does this, the female continues her assessment of his bower, decorations and his vocal mimicry.

    At some point, as indicated by some nuance of her behaviour, Red-over-white drops off the tree trunk to fly rapidly and in a serpentine flight path at the female

A female Golden Bowerbird approaches her nest, Paluma Range, north Queensland.

through the undergrowth as he rattles loudly. So taken by surprise is she that she takes off from the bower perch only an instant before otherwise being hit by the incoming yellow peril that is Red-over-white!

The vast majority of what we watched Red-over-white do that memorable day was new to science. Sadly that particular female continued to flee from his advances, and he returned to his bower shortly thereafter. But to our delight Red-over-white lived in excess of 20 years after we banded him, and surely must have been accepted by some females, but alas not in our presence. Red-over-green lived for a minimum of 14 years.

This story thus emphasises the joys, difficulties and good luck involved in attempting to learn the complete life history of even a single species of bowerbird: For to this day, our own many years of observation notwithstanding, no one has reported witnessing a pair of Golden Bowerbirds mating.

After 13 years at Paluma we learnt of a beautiful property for sale entirely covered with upland rainforest and home to Black-eared Catbirds, Tooth-billed, Satin, and Golden Bowerbirds, on the southern Atherton Tableland, near Cairns. We were fortunate enough to be able to obtain it and build our present home there. We continued to return to our study site at Paluma each year until 1998 in order to monitor and observe our banded birds until the vast majority of our 'golden oldies', including Red-over-white, had been replaced by unbanded ones of the next generation.

This book is our attempt to address the plethora of questions commonly asked about this biologically fascinating group of birds. Their architectural and artistic abilities, the history of their discovery, and their place in the cultural history and contemporary world of human beings are as absorbing to us as is their natural history. In our *Introduction* we briefly summarise the main points of interest about bowerbirds and hopefully impart some of what we find so fascinating, amusing, and absorbing about them.

An adult male Golden Bowerbird performs his courtship hiding display, Paluma Range, north Queensland.

".... There birds construct them shady bowers,
Deck'd with bright feathers, shells, and flowers ...."

[Extract from *The Southlanders* by M. Fox, 1860.]

INTRODUCTION

Naturalists have described the bowerbirds as the most remarkable, amazing, and even incredible, of all of birds on earth. This is because of the complexity of their structures known as 'bowers'. Male bowerbirds, uniquely within the nine to ten thousand species of birds living on earth today, skilfully build structures of sticks, grasses or other plant materials. They decorate these bowers with colourful fruits, flowers, feathers, skulls and other bones, stones, shells, dead insects, and numerous other natural, and also man-made, objects. Such decorative items may be present in numbers in excess of ten thousand on a single bower, although usually far fewer. Males of some species manufacture and apply paint to their bower walls, some birds even holding a wad of vegetable matter in the beak tip to use in a tool-like way in controlling the application of their paint. Because of this complex behaviour, bowerbirds have always been associated with high intelligence and exceptional artistic abilities and perception for animals as lowly as birds. So unusual are the various shapes and forms of bowers and so bizarre the related behaviour of the birds at them that some early ornithologists, people that study birds scientifically, suggested that bowerbirds should be placed in a class of their own, apart from all other birds.

The first bowers made known to science were the avenue bowers of both the Satin and Spotted Bowerbirds, described by John Gould, in 1840. The far more extraordinary maypole bower building habits of other bowerbirds first became known to the western world some 135 years ago. Biological specimen collector and botanist Odoardo (Otto) Beccari of Genoa, Italy, had spent a good deal of 1872 laboriously collecting plants and animals about the remote and rugged Vogelkop Peninsula of extreme western New Guinea, just south of the equator. In September of that year he undertook the intrepid hardship of ascending by foot into the cold and wet highlands of the Arfak Mountains, then unknown to Europeans. Together with his companion Count L.M. D'Albertis, Beccari had already been the first non Papuan to see living Masked Bowerbirds and had discovered several birds of paradise. As he made his way into the forests of the high Arfaks, however, the maypole bower structures built by bowerbirds remained entirely unknown to the western world. Small wonder, then, that when shown a skilfully built and architecturally complex large structure of orchid stems and mosses, artistically decorated with discrete piles of colourful flowers, fruits, and other items, he could not accept it as the work of a bird, as he was so assured by local Papuans. Instead he was convinced that such fabrication and artful design must surely have been the work of parent Papuans, built to entertain their small children; see the endpapers and Figure I.1.

So sophisticated are bower structures built by some bowerbird species that no inquisitive person could fail to be puzzled and intrigued by them. Once it was revealed and confirmed that these constructions and associated decorations were indeed the work of bowerbirds, intrigue turned to absorbed fascination, admiration,

Figure I.1 The first maypole bower made known to the western world was the roofed structure of the Vogelkop Bowerbird. From Otto Beccari's 1877 illustration with bower floor plan (opposite; see Further reading).

and awe. The eager study of them and their bowers inevitably followed quickly on the heels of their discovery and has continued, and increased exponentially, to the present time. Initial reports of the antics of bowerbirds attracted considerable attention because the gentry of Europe was then starting to take great interest in the accumulation and study of collections of natural history objects and facts. The latter part of the nineteenth and the early part of the twentieth centuries thus saw a dramatic increase in the numbers of professional field collectors seeking out skins of newly discovered species of bowerbirds for private and institutional collections.

The early discovery of several bowerbird species was inexorably connected to the bird of paradise 'plume trade'. Dried bird of paradise and some bowerbird skins have been traded within and beyond New Guinea for thousands if not tens

Figure I.2 The first bowerbird known to science, the Masked Bowerbird, was a colourful adult male at the time erroneously thought to be a bird of paradise. From Edwards, 1750, see Further reading.

of thousands of years, mostly for personal adornment. The first species made known to science, the Masked Bowerbird in 1750, was illustrated and described from a gloriously plumaged adult male; see Figure I.2. Because it came from New Guinea, and in view of its fabulous feather colouration, structure, and texture, many early ornithologists thought that it must be a member of the bird of paradise family; see Figure I.3 and Chapter 5. The second species described was the Regent Bowerbird, in 1808, and it was spectacularly colourful, and thus also bird of paradise-like; Figure I.4. It is therefore understandable that these two bowerbirds were not at the time appreciated as representing members of an entirely unknown new family of birds – the bowerbirds; see Chapter 5. The first drawing of a Regent Bowerbird's bower was made in 1861, Figure I.5, but bower-building behaviour was first made widely known to the western world by

Figure I.3 An adult (right) and subadult (left) male Red Bird of Paradise, showing how some birds of paradise are broadly similar in appearance to some bowerbirds (see Figure I.2). From Elliot, 1873, see Further reading.

Gold-crowned Honeyeater

F. Davies Delin.
1805

Figure I.4 The first, and previously unpublished, painting of an adult male Regent Bowerbird, erroneously thought to be a honeyeater at the time, by F. Davies in 1805 predates the formal description of the bird. By kind permission of the Natural History Museum, London.

Englishman John Gould the most famous 'Bird Man' of the British Empire in 1840. It was Gould who not only first called the structures built by these birds 'bowers' but also who first observed that the structures were used primarily for courtship. He stimulated much international interest in the bowerbirds and their doings.

For some 150 years ornithologists perceived the birds of paradise and the bowerbirds as constituting one single family, largely because of similarities in their geographical distributions, appearances, and behaviour. However, as growing evidence of major differences between the biology and behaviour of the bowerbirds compared with those of the birds of paradise became apparent several studies of their genetics confirmed the discrete status of the bowerbirds. Not only do the bowerbirds constitute a valid family but they form a highly distinctive one that is well removed from the birds of paradise among the world's songbirds.

Bowerbirds are found living only in Australia and New Guinea. In 1851 George R. Gray of the Natural History Museum in London established the bowerbird family. He named it the Ptilonorhynchidae, from the Greek, alluding to a partly feathered [ptilon] bill [rhunkhos]. It is one of the many families that constitute the great avian order of perching birds, that is scientifically termed the Passeriformes (or passerines). The family consists of 20 closely related species of stout, strong footed, typically fairly heavy-beaked, birds ranging in size from that of a little larger than a Common Starling to almost the size of an Australian Magpie. Nesting biology strategies within the bowerbird family are of great interest because the constituent species involve both monogamous (the

Figure I.5 The first, and previously unpublished, illustration of a Regent Bowerbird's bower; drawn on Ash Island, 22 September 1861, by one of the Harriett and Helena Scott sisters. By kind permission of the Mitchell Library, State Library of New South Wales.

three catbird species) and polygynous (the remaining 17 species) reproductive systems.

Both sexes of only the three catbird species (named for their wailing cat-like calls) form social pairs, to reproduce together during one or more years. Thus the catbirds practice monogamy, they are monogamous and thus reproduce monogamously. Whilst male catbirds do not assist with nest building, the incubation of eggs, or the brooding of their nestlings, both adult sexes share in the provisioning of food to their offspring. While they do not clear courts or build bowers catbirds share bowerbird skull, sperm, wing structure, and nesting biology characters that clearly mark them as bowerbird family members, and this has recently be confirmed by studies of their genetics.

Interest in the court-clearing Tooth-billed Bowerbird and the 16 bower building bowerbirds is intense because they are known or are presumed to practice polygyny, which is to be polygynous and thus reproduce polygynously. Males of the 17 polygynous species are promiscuous, attracting females to their court or bower site by calls and/or colourful plumage to there seduce and mate with as many as possible during each breeding season. Thus, courts and bowers are cleared, built, and maintained only by male bowerbirds that have nothing whatsoever to do with nests, eggs, nestlings and nesting in general. Females of all of the polygynous species nest build, incubate their eggs, and brood and provision their young alone and unaided by the father of their offspring. To the present day many people wrongly refer to bowers as nests and erroneously believe that these strutures have something to do with nesting. Thus in his 1909 book *The Heart of the Antarctic* Ernest Shackleton in describing the messy study and bedroom cubicle of Professor Thomas W. Edgeworth David, within their winter quarters hut, wrote of it as looking "like the nest of the Australian bower bird."

The bowerbirds are remarkable for the complex behaviour of males and the cultural, artistic, aesthetic, and architectural abilities that are associated with their bower building and courtship. Bowers can look like a diminutive thatched hut or tepee, a raised circular mossy bowl with a central conical tower of sticks, a four-walled open-topped 'box' of vertical stick walls, or a twin-walled 'avenue' of upright sticks. Not only are some bowers architecturally highly complex but also some reach more than three meters in height with a base area on many square meters. Adult males of some bower-building species are adorned with brilliantly colourful body plumage, crests, or capes, in marked contrast to their generally dull females and immature males. An important generalization is that bower-building bowerbird species with more colourful adult males build modest bowers whereas species having drabber males build larger and more complex structures.

The sophisticated building and decorating and related behaviour of bower-building males are all primarily to attract and impress females so that they might mate with them before they go off to nest independent of males. Male owners of courts and bowers constantly steal decorations from one another and also attempt to damage or destroy the bowers of rivals during raiding intrusions. Thus, males not only compete in the usual way but they acquire and accumulate bower decorations as a kind of 'wealth', which they then defend and try to steal from one another. In effect they construct symbols of their sexual prowess and status that are many times their own body size, and they decorate and paint them with great skill and care. Bowers and their accumulated decorations, often rare in nature, are indeed truly symbolic of each individual male's efforts and thus of his relative experience and thus age or survival or 'fitness' in the genetic sense. A bower represents characters of a male bowerbird's sexuality that are external to his body; Figure I.6. Male bowerbirds share this remarkable, and evolutionarily highly advanced, 'externalisation' of sexually attractive traits most conspicuously with human beings. People have always found other people adorned with, or with free access to larger quantities of, valued items impressive. Upon the arrival of a female at these symbols of relative male bowerbird attractiveness and fitness the males strut and dance complex steps and vocalise in an attempt to attain their all-important goal – a successful mating.

Bowerbirds have become the subjects of many exciting and instructive investigations, because they present some of the most easily studied elaborate male courtship traits found among birds. These display traits not only include highly ornate plumages, complex and often prolonged display posturing, choreography, and vocalizations, but also the suite of additional sexual characters that have become 'transferred' to their bower structures, decorations, and paint. The evolution and biological functions of these incredibly complex expressions of what Charles Darwin termed sexual selection, that bowers represent an expression of, have attracted intense interest over the past half a century. It is sexual selection, of male traits by females, that has brought about the amazing and uniquely complex behaviour of male bowerbirds we see today. That said some observers consider it possible that males may enjoy such activities for their own sake, because males often perform bower decoration and courtship behaviour in the absence of any audience; Figure I.7.

Recent bowerbird studies have included looking at degrees of sexual size and plumage differences, bower types and qualities, bower decorations, male-male interactions including bower decoration theft, nest sites and their dispersion, clutch sizes, general ecology and adult and nestling diets in particular, nesting success rates, periods of plumage maturity, visual and vocal courtship displays, and more. A fundamental finding emerging from field

Figure I.6 A complex roofed maypole bower of the Vogelkop Bowerbird with decorated mat beneath, Hungku, Anggi Lakes, Papua. By Will Betz.

25

work on variation in bowers and their decorations with regard to the relative mating success of their male owners is that females are selecting for several characters that are clearly indicative of male experience. It is known that younger males take at least five years to start to show initial small signs of adult plumage and even then remain far less capable of high quality vocalisations, displays or bower building than their elders. Years of experience are required, and the bowers symbolise the degree of this experience to females -- much as certificates of peoples' education symbolise their experience to potential employers. It may thus appear to be a case of jobs for the playboys in the world of bowerbirds but the life of male bowerbirds is actually far from a playful one. Life for them is one of constant and intense competition.

Adult-plumaged individuals represent but a small proportion of the total male population and the numerous immature males wearing female-like plumage persistently visit the bowers of their elders in order to learn indirectly from them and their structures and to, eventually, displace them. Very far from all males reaching adult plumage, and possibly even old age, get to reap the reward of access to numerous females to fertilise. In any local population of polygynous bowerbirds during each breeding season most females choose to mate with only the most attractive, dominant and fit individual(s). The other males struggle and wait for the opportunity to rise in male society to become a member of the reproducing class.

Figure I.7 An adult male Satin Bowerbird displays alone at his bower, as male bowerbirds will often do, Atherton Tableland, north Queensland.

INTRODUCTION

Of considerable significance is the new and novel finding of evidence suggesting that sexual selection by females for elaborate bowers correlates with increased brain size in male bowerbirds as compared to other Australasian songbirds of similar size and ecology. And, moreover, the bower-building species have larger brains than the non bower-building ones. This raises the question of whether mate choice by females has resulted in males having more grey matter that is specifically used for bower building and decorating or has resulted in generally smarter males!

Why people find bowerbird behaviour so amusing and absorbing should be clear from the above facts. Because of the intense interest that bowerbirds have generated ever since first made known the history of their discovery, appreciation, illustration, and study is a rich one. We write this book to make available to as wide a readership as possible a well-illustrated popular comprehensive account of the nature, art, and history of the bowerbirds. Our aims are to make the text easily readable to non biologists while at the same time covering aspects of the birds that are of significance to thier history and study of their biology and that are of interest within and, to some extent, beyond the bowerbird family. We review some aspects of the discovery of bowerbirds and their biology herein for the first time and include a number of illustrations of them previously unpublished. In keeping with our aims we do not insert citations to authors and years of publication of literature alluded to (*i.e.* Frith & Frith 2004) or read by us (*i.e.* Darwin 1874), as in more formal writing. We provide full citations to only more important and substantial general bowerbird literature, or to titles mentioned in the text, under *Further reading*. For readers wishing to find more bibliographic detail relating to the bowerbirds the publication to be consulted is *The Bowerbirds – Ptilonorhynchidae*, published in 2004 by Oxford University Press, and written by the present authors.

The vast island of New Guinea is politically divided into two: The easten half, closest to Australia, is independant (since 1975) Papua New Guinea. Western New Guinea (Dutch New Guinea during 1828 to 1962), is now a province of Indonesia that has been known by various names including Irian Jaya, West Papua and Papua and it is the latter we use in this book. It is hoped that the present comprehensive review might lead some readers to seek more biological details, insights, and theoretical considerations of the bowerbirds.

The following Chapters 1 to 6 go into greater detail about all aspects of the lives of these birds: the first four chapters that are Part I of the book *Bowerbirds and their nature* deal with their origins and natural history, the two chapters comprising Part II *Bowerbirds and people* details early bowerbird discoveries and reviews relationships between people and bowerbirds, and Chapter 7 that is Part III, *The bowerbird family* presents summaries of all that is factually known about the 20 different bowerbird species. We have intentionally made these species accounts comprehensively detailed rather than provide an incomplete coverage of the birds' biology merely for the sake of brevity.

PART I

THE BOWERBIRDS AND THEIR NATURE

An adult male Satin Bowerbird at his bower, Atherton Tableland, north Queensland.

1

Origins and features of the bowerbirds

Much is written about the evolution of the perching birds of Australasia. Scientists long considered the birds of this region to have their origins in or via Southeast Asia. It was therefore concluded that what was then seen as the 'bird of paradise and bowerbird group' derived from a single colonisation of New Guinea by an old bird lineage of Asiatic or even African origin. More recent research indicates, however, that some 85 percent of the Australasian perching birds, including the bird of paradise and bowerbird and other 'old endemic' families, have a southern, or Gondwanan, origin.

Australia and New Guinea share a common avifaunal history because their landscapes have a common origin in the prehistoric southern continent of Gondwana and subsequent geological events. The latter involved the rifting of the Australian Plate from the great southern icebound continent Gondwana some 160 million years ago, although it did not become an island continent until some 45 million years ago. As the Australian Plate split away from Antarctica it carried part of the Gondwanan flora and fauna, appropriately described as the Gondwana ark. The present day southern part of New Guinea was at that time the northern front of the northward-moving Australian continent, but for most of Australia's isolated northerly drift into warmer latitudes it was submerged. It is thought that 40 to 30 million years ago Australia was extensively rainforested.

Australia continued to drift in isolation towards warmer latitudes until some 20 to 15 million years ago, when two major events occurred coincidentally. The first involved Australia becoming increasingly drier during its northerly drift, slowly at first and then more rapidly. Ancient rainforests began contracting to be replaced by a much drier landscape with sclerophyll woodlands dominated by *Eucalyptus* and *Acacia* trees, grassland, savanna, and arid shrublands thus allowing the successful radiation of some wet forest-dwelling bowerbirds to successfully occupy the open habitats of inland Australia, notably the grey bowerbirds. The second event was the collision of the Australian-New Guinean Plate with the northern Pacific one, this causing the beginning of the uplifting of the New Guinea mountain ranges. As the mountains rose over geological time ancient Gondwana ark rainforest elements, including some bowerbirds, became isolated at higher altitudes as new biogeographical elements invaded New Guinea from the north. The remainder of present New Guinea emerged about five million years ago, when it was no longer connected to Australia.

Contact between Australia and New Guinea was restored intermittently during some 17 glacial periods, or ices ages, that started about two-and-a-half million years ago, during the Pleistocene. During colder glacial periods, sea levels dropped and land bridges were exposed across the Torres Strait, so that northern Australia and southern New Guinea became connected. Many bird species on Cape York Peninsula today, such as the Fawn-breasted Bowerbird, are thought to have evolved in New Guinea but now retain an outlier distribution on the north-eastern tip of Australia.

Bowerbirds belong to a broad radiation of birds that occurred in Australasia during the past 60 million years, and possibly diverged from close Australian lyrebird and scrub-bird relatives about 45 million years ago. Recent biomolecular researchers suggested that the separation of bowerbirds from crow-like relatives, including the birds of paradise, occurred some 28 million years ago and that major lineages within the bowerbird family arose 24 million years ago. The Satin Bowerbird is presently the only bowerbird known in the fossil record: Fossil Satin Bowerbirds have been found in the east and southwest of the Australian state of Victoria, from the geological epochs of the Pleistocene and Holocene of the Quaternary sub era. These fossils testify to the previously far greater extent of Australian wet forests than exist today, and that are now predominantly restricted to the central eastern and north-eastern seaboard of the continental island.

Today, bowerbirds occur only on the vast island of New Guinea, the island continent of Australia and a few immediately adjacent islands.

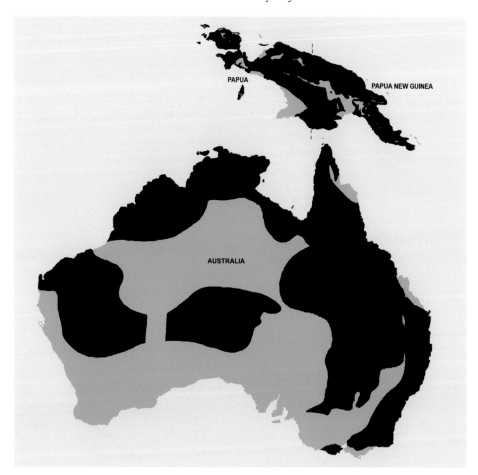

Bowerbirds are restricted to parts of New Guinea and Australia, and some of their islands, as indicated by the black areas.

The bowerbird family

Approximately ten thousand bird species are living on earth today. Of these forty percent constitute the evolutionarily more primitive group known as the non-perching birds or the non-passerines that are mostly the larger bodied and more ground frequenting birds. The other sixty percent of all birds are the smaller, evolutionarily more advanced, perching or passerine birds. They are so named because they are better anatomically adapted to life perching in trees. It is the perching birds that the bowerbird family, the Ptilonorhynchidae, belongs to. The perching birds are anatomically subdivided into a more primitive group, scientifically termed the Tyranni or suboscines, and a more advanced group called the Passeri or oscines. This fundamental division is based in large part upon the physical construction of the syrinx, which accounts for the more advanced oscines being known as the 'songbirds' because their more evolutionarily advanced syrinx enables them to produce more complex song. Bowerbirds are medium-sized members of the oscine perching songbirds.

The, taxonomic or systematic, position of the bowerbirds within the songbirds as a whole was unsettled through history until recent decades; this situation reflecting uncertainty among ornithologists about bowerbirds' origins and their relationships to other birds. Bowerbirds had long been most closely associated with the birds of paradise but a growing body of evidence indicated major differences between the two groups and several subsequent studies of their genetics confirmed the discrete status of the bowerbirds not only as a valid family but also as a highly distinctive one. Of late the lyrebirds, a peculiarly Australian bird family including only two lyrebird species, have been considered the birds most close to bowerbirds by some, but by no means all, ornithologists; Figure 1.1. Current consensus is that the bowerbird family represents a basal, or primitive, group within the songbirds. Bowerbirds have certain characters of their legs, feet, palate, syrinx, sperm, and behaviour that together define them as a distinct family but none of which is unique to them as a group. While bowerbird anatomy is, however, broadly typical of the perching birds, there are a couple of notable exceptions. An enlarged lachrymal, a part of the cranium bone structure near the eye socket, represents a skull character that is unique to the bowerbird family within the perching birds and that is otherwise paralleled only in the lyrebirds. Also conspicuously different are the larger numbers of 11 to 14 secondaries, the inner wing flight feathers, that oocur in bowerbirds than do so in the majority of other perching birds that have only 9 to 10.

The family consists of 20 species that are divided into eight natural sub groupings, each consisting of what is known as a genus (genera in the plural) - these being: the **catbirds**; the **Tooth-billed Bowerbird**; the **gardener bowerbirds** (the four species of *Amblyornis*); **Archbold's**; the **Golden**; the **silky bowerbirds** (the four species of *Sericulus*); the **Satin Bowerbird**; and the five **grey bowerbirds** (the species of *Chlamydera*). The 20 different bowerbirds include three monogamous species and 17 polygynous ones (see page 52). Of the latter the

Tooth-billed Bowerbird clears a court while the remainder are grouped according to the kind of bower stucture they build as indicated in the boxed feature text.

Appearance and longevity

Bowerbirds vary in size from 22 to 37 centimetres in total body length, beak to tail tip, and from plump and stocky to slender in body shape. The smallest of them is the Golden Bowerbird with adults averaging 80 grams. The Great Bowerbird is the largest, with adults averaging 200 grams. Adult female catbirds average almost 10 percent lighter than their adult males in weight. In most other bowerbirds the adult females are usually slightly smaller than their respective adult males, but in three of the four silky bowerbirds adult females average the same size to slightly larger than adult males.

Most bowerbird species have a relatively short, deep, and robust beak and

1.1. An adult male Albert's Lyrebird *Menura alberti* in courtship display, Lamington, Queensland. By Glen Threlfo.

1.2 An adult Black-eared Catbird, Paluma Range, north Queensland.

stout, powerful, legs and feet. Silky bowerbirds are exceptional, however, in having relatively longer and finer beaks, particularly so the Regent Bowerbird that eats much flower nectar. The Tooth-billed Bowerbird is unique among its family in having a conspicuous notch or 'tooth' on the cutting edges of its upper beak and several cusps and notches on the tip and cutting edges of its lower beak; see Chapter 2.

Beaks of bowerbirds are dark brown, blackish or black, with those of adult males of some sexually dimorphic species showing some colour. Adult males of gardener and silky bowerbirds have a pale bluish base to the lower beak, while the entire bill is pale in adult male Satins and is whitish in both sexes of

1.3 An adult male Tooth-billed Bowerbird singing above his court, Paluma Range, north Queensland (opposite).

1.4 An adult male Macgregor's Bowerbird, Tari Valley slopes, Papua New Guinea.

all catbirds. Adult male Regent Bowerbirds have a bright orange-yellow bill. Mouth colour is black in adult catbirds. In adult male Tooth-billed Bowerbirds the mouth is black, with a sharply contrasting white anterior to the upper beak interior, while in all other individuals of the species the mouth is pale yellowish-flesh. The mouth colour in most other bowerbirds for which it is recorded is orange-yellow or yellowish.

Adult bowerbird eye, or iris, colour is most often dark to pale brown and is similar but paler and greyer, in juveniles. It is, however, red in adult catbirds and blue-grey in their juveniles. The Golden, silky, and Satin bowerbirds share a pale adult male eye colour, that of the latter species being strikingly blue. While eye colour is typically brown in female silky bowerbirds some apparently older individual female Regent Bowerbirds may show variable amounts of yellow intruding into it. Bowerbirds legs and feet are typically dark brownish, olive-brown, olive, blue-grey or blackish, but are a paler and brighter grey-blue in catbirds, are distinctly blue in the Vogelkop Bowerbird, and are a much paler tan colour in Satin Bowerbirds.

While the bowerbirds form a group of closely related and generally more similar looking species, in terms of their body proportions, posture, and general appearance, than do the members of many perching bird families they

1.5 An adult male Archbold's Bowerbird, Tari Gap, Papua New Guinea (opposite).

do include some strikingly diverse plumages. In simple terms, the bowerbird family exhibits some 50 to 60 different plumages, given that each of most of the 20 species includes a juvenile and an adult male and female, and some a distinctive subadult male, plumage. See Figures 1.2 to 1.11 for some of them.

Adult males and females of all three catbirds and the Tooth-billed, Vogelkop, and grey bowerbirds are identical or nearly so, which technically is to say that they are sexually monomorphic or of the same appearance. Thus both sexes of of catbirds are similarly green above and spotted or streaked green to buff below with conspicuously contrasting black and white facial markings and those of Tooth-billed and Vogelkop Bowerbirds are identically generally brown. In contrast, the other polygynous bowerbirds are dramatically sexually dimorphic, in plumage, their adult males being dressed in brilliantly coloured plumage, decorated with an ornate crest or cape, while their females are drab. Adult males of the other three and otherwise brown, gardener bowerbirds (the Vokelkop Bowerbird being the forth), and the all black Archbold's Bowerbird, wear erectile crests of bright orange or yellow. Unlike the closely related gardener bowerbirds, adult male Golden Bowerbirds are largely brilliant yellow while their females, and immature males, are greyish. Adult male silky bowerbirds are brilliantly plumaged in contrasting areas of black and intense reds or yellows while their females, and immature males, are cryptically plumaged and are ventrally barred.

1.6 An adult male Golden Bowerbird, Paluma Range, north Queensland (opposite).

1.7 An adult male Regent Bowerbird, Lamington, Queensland.

Other than being generally green the plumages of female, and immature male, Satin Bowerbirds are intermediate in characters between those of the silky and grey bowerbirds. The five grey bowerbirds are grey to brown, with the sexes near identical save that in some males have larger crests than females.

Bowerbird nestlings wear long, dense down in large patches on their crown, wings, and body; see Chapter 4. This is reddish grey-brown in catbirds, greyish-brown in Tooth-billed and gardener bowerbirds, dark greyish-brown in Archbold's

1.8 An adult male Satin Bowerbird adds sticks to his bower, Atherton Tableland, north Queensland.

and Golden Bowerbirds, and a much paler grey in Satin, Regent, and the grey bowerbirds. This down makes the pale-skinned (pinkish, orange-pink, or pale flesh colour) nestlings less visible in the nest and presumably it also provides insulation. This natal down of nestlings is replaced by a juvenile plumage much like that of their respective adult females but slightly duller and softer-textured and typically more barred on the underparts in the avenue builders; Figure 1.10. An even more adult-female-like plumage replaces the juvenile plumage with the first annual moult, or change of feathers. In only a few species is the latter plumage discernable as being that of a young male rather than that of an adult female; see Figure 1.11. To attain adult male plumage may take a surprising number of years.

Attainment of adult male characters

Several perching birds in which their promiscuous males court at traditional focal displaying sites, such as courts or bowers, exhibit a delayed acquisition of adult male characters. Young male Tooth-billed Bowerbirds have pale mouth interiors and may take four years or more to attain the black colour of their elders, even after establishing a court. Other so-called soft part colours,

1.9 An adult male Spotted Bowerbird with a stone bower decoration, one of the five species of grey bowerbird, Charters Towers, Queensland.

1.10 A brood of Spotted Bowerbird nestlings, near fledging age, wear adult-like plumage but with down still attached to some feathers, Charters Towers, Queensland.

including the beak, eyes, legs and feet, also change with age, as mentioned above. Bower-building bowerbirds show similar trends, with a large proportion of non-breeding immature males wearing female-like plumage for some six or seven years before acquiring their adult dress. Thus, immature male bowerbirds move about populations of their own kind for more than half a decade before showing any sign of adult plumage, and thus their sex. Their subsequent subadult plumage, at some six or seven year-old, also signals that they are not yet fully part of the more competitive society of adult males. This prolonged period spent dressed in plumages other than that of adult males has advantages. It may well enhance the young males' opportunities to move about bower sites of adult males and so gain valuable experience before 'showing their true colours' and suffering the aggressive consequences. Moreover, as immature male plumages are cryptic the deferral of bright adult plumage presumably also reduces the risks of younger males attracting the attention of predators.

Male bowerbirds may attain their brightly coloured adult plumage by it increasingly intruding into the female-like immature plumage, that they have worn for the past five or six years, over one or two moulting seasons; see Figure 1.12. It can, on the other hand, be attained in its entirety during a single moult.

This is markedly different to males of most perching birds, possibly including the catbirds, which attain adult plumage and breed within their first year of two of life. In contrast to the males of polygynous bowerbird species their females appear to usually sexually mature and reproduce at a far younger age.

1.11 The adult female plumage of the Regent Bowerbird is identical to that worn by younger immature males, Lamington, Queensland (above left).

1.12 A male Regent Bowerbird in subadult plumage, Lamington, Queensland (above right).

Survivorship

Average annual bowerbird survival rates are extremely high for songbirds, and are particularly so in bower owning adult males: Thus male Tooth-billed and Golden Bowerbirds that we studied over 19 consecutive seasons enjoyed an annual survival rate of at least 90 percent and an average expectation of further life of more than nine years after we had first caught and banded them. Some individual Black-eared Catbirds that we caught and marked lived to at least 19 years and males of polygynous bowerbird species that we studied lived 20 or more, and one up to 27, years. A female Golden Bowerbird lived at least 14 years after we had caught and banded her as a breeding adult.

While individual bowerbirds may live to a ripe old age others obviously suffer predation. There are many reptile, bird, and mammal species that could not only take eggs or nestlings from bowerbirds' nests but also a nest-attending parent, or could predate males as they are attending their bowers. Records of predators actually doing so are, however, few. In response to the presence of a potential predator closeby adult bowerbirds at their courts, bowers, or nests will stike motionless or 'frozen' postures in order to avoid detection. If detected, however, parents at their nests may perform distraction displays; see Chapters 4 and 7.

Distribution and habitats

Ten of the 20 species are restricted to mainland New Guinea, eight species to Australia, and two species live on both New Guinea and Australia. Only White-eared and Black-eared Catbirds and the Great Bowerbird are known to occupy offshore, continental, islands. Bowerbirds occur predominantly within the tropics and subtropics with only the Satin, and to lesser extent the Spotted, Bowerbird ranging significantly southward into temperate Australia; see Figure 1.1.

Bowerbirds, including the three catbirds, the Tooth-billed, Golden, gardener, and Archbold's Bowerbirds, are predominantly confined to wet forests. The silky and Satin Bowerbirds occupy rainforests, but also strongly associate with rainforest edges, and the latter species also with adjacent wet sclerophyll woodlands. The five grey bowerbirds are the only real exception to wet forest or rainforest dwelling. They have adapted to the drier and more open environments of riverine forests, open woodlands, savannas, forest-grassland communities and,

1.13 Wet tropical rainforests and Mt. Bartle Frere, north Queensland, home to the Black-eared Catbird, Tooth-billed, Golden and Satin Bowerbirds.

in Australia, to near desert. Interestingly, Lauterbach's Bowerbird of upland New Guinea and the Fawn-breasted Bowerbird of lowland New Guinea and extreme north-eastern Australia show intermediate habitat preference: These two species live at the edges, or within mosaics, of rainforest-grassland and rainforest-woodland communities respectively. As a generalisation, those bowerbird species with colourful adult male plumage are predominantly inhabitants of denser forest habitats while the males of species inhabiting grasslands, drier woodlands, and arid habitats are largely dully plumaged and looking like their respective females. For more details and maps of distributions of the various species; see Chapter 7.

In Australia six bowerbird species live in the tropics and subtropics, mostly within rainforests, at varying altitudes along the eastern escarpments and summits of the Great Dividing Range and the coastal lowlands. In contrast, the four grey bowerbirds inhabit drier habitats predominantly to the west of the Great Divide. Many species are not adverse to exploiting human environments, including suburban parks, gardens, orchards, and homesteads if water and suitable food plants are available. It is within the Australian rainforests that most bowerbirds occur together, involving both monogamous and polygynous species. Tropical upland rainforests are the shared home of the Black-eared Catbird, Tooth-bill, Golden, and the small northern form or subspecies of the Satin Bowerbird. The

1.14 Wet subtropical rainforest, Lamington National Park, Queensland, home of the Green Catbird, Regent and Satin Bowerbirds.

1.15 Inland Australia is grey bowerbird country; this being near Finke River and the MacDonnell Range, Northern Territory, where Western Bowerbirds occur.

1.16 Upland New Guinea grassland/rainforest mosaic habitat of the Fawn-breasted Bowerbird; Jimi Valley, Papua New Guinea.

latter three are mostly confined to areas 600 metres or more above sea level; Figure 1.13. The Black-eared Catbird also occurs in lowland areas, including Hinchinbrook Island, and further north on eastern Cape York Peninsula. The Golden Bowerbird occurs above about 350, more typically 680, metres and up to 1260 metres on Mount Bartle Frere, the highest altitude for any bowerbird in Australia.

The Green Catbird and Regent Bowerbird primarily inhabit rainforest interiors within the subtropics while the Satin Bowerbird there is mostly a rainforest edge species that also inhabits adjacent eucalypt sclerophyll forests and woodland. Green Catbirds, Regent, and Satin Bowerbirds occur in both subtropical uplands, Figure 1.14, and lowlands. Satins extend further south into the temperate rainforests of the Otway Ranges of Victoria. These three species do co-exist in habitats of some areas.

The four Australian grey bowerbirds inhabit drier tropical and subtropical sclerophyll habitats, mostly west of the Great Divide. Habitats vary from eucalypt-dominated open forests to woodlands with melaleucas, sclerophyll shrubs, and grassy understoreys. These landscapes are dissected with, most often dry, river systems lined with dense to sparse riverine vegetation; Figure 1.15. The Fawn-breasted Bowerbird is a New Guinea species with a small outlier distribution on Cape York Peninsula, where it inhabits pockets and galleries of vine forests, eucalypt woodlands, and mangrove-grassland mosaics. The Fawn-breasted and Great Bowerbird both occur on northern Cape York Peninsula. Where they occur together the Fawn-breasted Bowerbird is more frequently found in mangroves or adjacent melaleuca-dominated habitats, while Great Bowerbirds prefer open woodland. The Great Bowerbird also occurs extensively across the northern tropics as well as extending further south in north-eastern Australia on the east of the Great Divide where suitable habitat exists. Its bowers are commonly built in riverine vegetation adjacent to riverbeds.

Habitats of the tropics west of Australia's Great Dividing Range become increasingly drier. Areas change from eucalypt-dominated woodland to *Acacia* woodlands and shrublands mixed with low shrublands and grasslands. This type of semi-arid to arid habitat extends into the subtropics of central and western tropical Australia. Spotted and Western Bowerbirds occur in these regions. Spotted Bowerbirds favour open woodland with low dense shrubbery, under which males build their bowers. Western Bowerbirds replace Spotted Bowerbirds in central and western Australia, the former favouring areas close to water such as river gorges with shady copses, and Rock Fig fruit availability to some extent dictates the distribution of Western Bowerbirds in more arid areas, as they represent an important food resource to them; see Chapter 2.

The 10 bowerbird species in New Guinea primarily live within humid forests but the two grey bowerbirds found there live in drier and/or more open habitats. One or both catbirds in New Guinea may occur together along with one or more species of polygynous bowerbird. Lauterbach's has a wide attitudinal range from lowland to lower and mid-montane areas. The

1.17 Hill forest habitat of
Macgregor's and Adelbert
Bowerbirds, Adelbert Range,
Papua New Guinea.

1.18 Moss forest habitat
of Archbold's Bowerbird
interspersed with grassland, Tari
Gap, Papua New Guinea.
This was the authors' main study
area in New Guinea.

Fawn-breasted Bowerbird is, however, primarily a lowland species although locally common at elevations at about 1100 metres and rarely to 1700 metres; Figure 1.16. Four pairs of closely related polygynous bowerbird species meet in New Guinea where their, otherwise predominantly separate, altitudinal ranges abut or overlap and they cohabit over a limited altitudinal belt. Because of the great mountain ranges of New Guinea bowerbird species there are segregated by altitude, each living within different forest types of one or more distinct altitudinal zones: White-eared Catbirds and Flame Bowerbirds occur mainly in lowland rainforests. Lowland dwelling White-eared Catbirds are replaced in hill forest by Black-eared Catbirds, the two occurring together in some limited areas. The Masked Bowerbird replaces the Flame Bowerbird at higher altitudes of the lower montane forests. The Streaked Bowerbird also lives primarily within the lower montane forest. Macgregor's Bowerbird replaces the Streaked Bowerbird at higher altitudes of the mid-montane forest. The forests of the Adelbert Range are shared by Macgregor's and Adelbert Bowerbirds; Figure 1.17. Vogelkop and Yellow-fronted Bowerbirds also occur primarily in mid-montane forests, as does Archbold's Bowerbird, at altitudes above 1750 metres. Archbold's Bowerbird predominantly occurs above the altitudinal range of Macgregor's Bowerbird, but the two do occur together at least in forest just below Tari Gap in Papua New Guinea. This is often referred to as cloud or moss forest, and higher patches of it are often interspersed with grasslands; Figure 1.18. Archbold's Bowerbird is recorded at 2850 to 3660 metres above sea level in the Ilaga Valley of Papua, the highest altitude recorded for any living bowerbird.

Hybridisation

In some cases where the ranges of two closely related polygynous bowerbird species that share similar habitats overlap they might hybridise, but only rarely. Geographically restricted cases of hybridisation have been confirmed between Macgregor's and Streaked, and between Masked and Flame Bowerbirds in New Guinea, and between Great and Spotted Bowerbirds in northern Queensland, Australia. In such circumstances the bowers of one bowerbird species population may have their structure influenced by the building activities of males of another species; see Chapter 7.

In 1867 a unique specimen of an adult male bowerbird, shot in Brisbane and known as Rawnsley's Bowerbird, looked like it may have been the result of hybridisation between a Satin and a Regent Bowerbird, Figure 1.19. Unfortunately the stuffed specimen of this unique bird disappeared, but a review of its history and appearance led to it being considered to have most likely been the result of the proposed hybridisation, and far less likely to be an aberrant Satin Bowerbird as was also suggested. Regent and Satin Bowerbirds may be found visiting each other's bowers in a few places where they occur in the same habitat, such as at Lamington National Park south of Brisbane. In recent decades bird watchers occasionally observed individuals of these two

1.19 Rawnsley's Bowerbird was described as a good species in 1867 but is now known to be the result of hybridisation between Satin and Regent Bowerbirds. The painting is from J. Gould's 1869 *The Birds of Australia, Supplement.*

species visiting bowers of one another; Figure 1.20. But only as recently as 2005 was it confirmed in print that a Satin Bowerbird and a Regent Bowerbird have indeed cross-bred to produce a hybrid individual. Thus this cross breeding of two individuals, not only from two different species but also representing two genera, is confirmed to have occured on at least two occasions 136 years apart; see Figure 1.21.

There remains the possibility that one or more other hybrid bowerbird combinations, such as between Fawn-breasted and Great Bowerbirds that cohabit on parts of Cape York Peninsula, northeastern Australia, and between

1.20 An adult male Satin Bowerbird, in background, adds a bunch of flowers to his bower as an adult male Regent Bowerbird arrives at his bower intent upon stealing some of his decorations, Lamington, Queensland.

Lauterbach's and Fawn-breasted Bowerbirds that co-exist on the Ramu River of northern Papua New Guinea, remain to be discovered. Even the potential for hybridisation between Macgregor's and Archbold's Bowerbirds must be conceded.

With their evolutionary origins in the geological past of their remote corner of the globe, the 20 bowerbird species of today continued to live out their complex lives largely unknown to western science. The next three chapters comprehensively detail what is now known about the biology of the incredible bowerbirds.

1.21 A living 'Rawnsley's Bowerbird' in foreground, with a female-plumaged Satin Bowerbird behind, previously only known from a unique and now lost stuffed specimen; Binna Burra, Queensland. By and courtesy of Dan Blunt.

The 20 bowerbird species, their general distribution and court or bower types

Common names	Scientific names	Court or bower types	
THE MONOGAMOUS CATBIRDS			
White-eared Catbird (NG)	*Ailuroedus buccoides*	**None**	
Black-eared Catbird (NG & Aust)	*Ailuroedus melanotis*	**None**	Catbirds
Green Catbird (Aust)	*Ailuroedus crassirostris*	**None**	
THE POLYGYNOUS BOWERBIRDS			
Tooth-billed Bowerbird (Aust)	*Scenopoeetes dentirostris*	**Court**	
Macgregor's Bowerbird (NG)	*Amblyornis macgregoriae*	**Maypole**	
Streaked Bowerbird (NG)	*Amblyornis subalaris*	**Maypole**	Gardener
Vogelkop Bowerbird (NG)	*Amblyornis inornatus*	**Maypole**	bowerbirds
Yellow-fronted Bowerbird (NG)	*Amblyornis flavifrons*	**Maypole**	
Archbold's Bowerbird (NG)	*Archboldia papuensis*	**Maypole**	
Golden Bowerbird (Aust)	*Prionodura newtoniana*	**Maypole**	
Masked Bowerbird (NG)	*Sericulus aureus*	**Avenue**	
Flame Bowerbird (NG)	*Sericulus ardens*	**Avenue**	Silky
Adelbert Bowerbird (NG)	*Sericulus bakeri*	**Avenue**	bowerbirds
Regent Bowerbird (Aust)	*Sericulus chrysocephalus*	**Avenue**	
Satin Bowerbird (Aust)	*Ptilonorhynchus violaceus*	**Avenue**	
Lauterbach's Bowerbird (NG)	*Chlamydera lauterbachi*	**Avenue**	
Fawn-breasted Bowerbird (NG & Aust)	*Chlamydera cerviniventris*	**Avenue**	Grey
Spotted Bowerbird (Aust)	*Chlamydera maculata*	**Avenue**	bowerbirds
Western Bowerbird (Aust)	*Chlamydera guttata*	**Avenue**	
Great Bowerbird (Aust)	*Chlamydera nuchalis*	**Avenue**	

(NG= New Guinea, Aust = Australia)

2

Bowerbird ecology

Annual bowerbird court or bower establishment, attendance, courtship, mating, nesting, and feather replacement are in large part governed by climate. Climatic conditions are reflected in the relative availability of the food resources critical to sustaining birds through these energetically demanding aspects of their annual life cycles. The availability of food and particularly of fruit, the major component of bowerbirds' diets, in time and space is the main factor dictating the kind of mating system employed and home range size. It also profoundly affects the annual seasonality of bower attendance by males and the timing of various aspects of breeding activity.

Annual cycles of bowerbirds in New Guinea are little understood, not only because information is limited but also because of the great range of climatic regimes existing over their extensive geographical and altitudinal ranges. Much more is known for Australian species, however, particular for those living in humid forests. It is longer-term studies of Black-eared Catbirds, Tooth-bill, Golden, and Satin Bowerbirds living together in upland rainforests of the Australian tropics, and of Green Catbirds, Regent, and Satin Bowerbirds together in upland subtropical forests, that provide the information in this chapter.

The marked wet and dry seasons of Australian rainforests dictate bowerbird annual cyclic events. The relative availability of foods varies from year to year, corresponding to wet season rains and the severity of the dry season. This in turn affects the commencement, length, and termination, of the various phases of bowerbird annual cycles and the degree of success in producing offspring. For the catbirds, Tooth-billed, Golden, Regent, and Satin Bowerbirds the courtship display and nesting seasons start as annual temperatures initially rise, typically during August to early September. But males sometimes commence their activities at bowers as early as June to July, especially at lower, and thus warmer, altitudes. Peak display and nesting is mostly during late September to December, when temperatures and rainfall increase and fruit, flying insects, and forest floor leaf litter invertebrates are most abundant. Activities at bowers and nests terminate with the onset of heavy wet season rains. Nestlings leave nests immediately before or during the early wet season rains. Food resources remain abundant during the wetter months. The latter period is when parents are provisioning their fledglings. Annual wing, tail, and body, feather replacement in adult bowerbirds mainly occurs during December to March, and peaks during the wetter months of January to March, after their young have left the nest. Toward the end of the moult, immediately prior to the annually drier,

cooler, and leanest period within their habitats in terms of food abundance, bowerbird body weight and fat increases.

Far less is known about life history cycles, in relation to climate and food availability, in the more open habitat dwelling grey bowerbirds. Their display and breeding seasons are strongly influenced by seasonal, but far less predictable, rainfall. Certainly fluctuations in insect populations and particularly those of grasshoppers and locusts, which peak after rains because of resultant new leaf growth, strongly influence the timing and length of annual grey bowerbird courtship and breeding. The availability of fruits of the Rock Fig is also important in many areas; see *Diet and foraging* below.

The display and nesting seasons of the grey bowerbirds are much longer than those of species in wet forests, but their extent varies geographically. As a generalisation, their bowers are annually attended by July, but in some areas this can be as early as April, with activity at bowers continuing through November or December. Peak nesting months usually precede the annual monsoonal rains; see Chapter 4. Grey bowerbirds usually moult towards the end of the calendar year following courtship and nesting, but some individuals moult wing and tail feathers at other times. That they have protracted breeding seasons, particularly in more arid environments, suggests the possibility of overlap between their annual breeding and moult.

Diet and foraging

Bowerbirds eat a great diversity of both plant and animal foods – and are therefore said to be dietary generalists or omnivores. Because fruits form the basis of bowerbirds' diets, especially so those living in rainforest, their foraging mainly occurs in the forest canopy but they do also feed in the subcanopy and understorey or even on the ground to take both fruits and animals from the leaf litter; Figures 2.1 to 2.3.

Bowerbirds select fruits for their nutritional value, size, texture, colour, or the ease of harvesting them. Basic fruit structure is, however, also important. Bowerbirds predominantly eat simple berry, or drupe, fruits including figs, as opposed to better-protected 'capsular' fruits that require greater manipulative skills to obtain. They do not use their feet to hold and manipulate foods and are thus unable to easily extract the edible reward from the complex protective husks of capsular fruits. They will, however, take fruit from some protective capsules as they become accessible; Figures 2.1 and 2.6. Large fruits, such as those of some figs and climbing-pandans, Figure 2.7, are torn apart and eaten in situ. Australian dry-country grey bowerbirds are particularly fond of the fruits of the Rock Fig.

In Australian tropical rainforests fruits represent 80 to 90 percent of total diets of Black-eared Catbirds, Tooth-billed, and Golden Bowerbirds but in subtropical rainforest Green Catbirds, Regent, and Satin Bowerbirds eat fruits as 65 to 80 percent of their intake. This difference could reflect a greater diversity of suitable fruits in tropical rainforests. Rainforest dwelling bowerbirds also feed

2.1 A Toothbill-billed Bowerbird forages in a fruiting nutmeg tree, Paluma Range, north Queensland.

2.2 An adult male Regent Bowerbird forages in a fig tree, Lamington, Queensland.

2.3 Black-eared Catbirds often visit the forest floor to forage, as this bird at Paluma Range, north Queensland.

a large proportion of fruit to their nestlings; see Chapter 4 and Figures 2.8 and 2.9.

Beside fruits, Australian rainforest bowerbirds also eat leaves and flowers and their stems, buds, stamens, pollen and nectar in situ. Seeds and sap are also eaten to varying but limited extent. For details of the diets of the individual species see Chapter 7. Regent Bowerbirds include a large proportion of flower product in their diet, but take mostly nectar. Their longer and finer bills are better adapted to this feeding upon flower nectar than are those of other

2.4 A simple fruit of the kind known as a drupe is the White Supplejack *Ripogonum album*, Paluma Range, north Queensland (top left).

2.5 A fruiting Rusty Fig, *Ficus destruens*, Paluma Range, north Queensland (top right).

2.6 Capsular fruits of the Yellow Boxwood *Xanthophyllum octandrum*, Paluma Range, north Queensland (centre left).

2.7 A large ripe Slender Climbing-pandan fruit, *Freycinetia excelsa,* Paluma Range, north Queensland (centre right).

2.8 Adult Black-eared Catbird about to feed a Fuzzy Lemon Aspen fruit, *Acronychia vestita*, to its nestling, near Paluma Range, north Queensland.

2.9 An adult female Golden Bowerbird about to feed her nestlings Northern Yellow Carabeen fruits, *Slonea macbrydei*, near, Paluma Range, north Queensland.

2.10 The Regent Bowerbird has a relatively longer, finer, beak than any other bowerbird, Lamington, Queensland.

bowerbirds; Figure 2.10. Female Regents have been observed to chase others of their kind from flowers, suggesting that nectar represents a resource of sufficient value to them to be worth their defending. Satin Bowerbirds feed upon banksia and grevillea nectar and the leaves and flowers of many herbaceous plants. In drier habitats, Spotted, Western and grey bowerbirds eat the flowers and buds of *Acacia* and *Eucalyptus* trees; Figure 2.11.

Australian rainforest dwelling bowerbirds, except perhaps the Golden, eat some leaf matter as well as succulent leaf buds, stems, and/or vine tendrils. Leaves form a major part of Tooth-billed and Satin Bowerbirds winter diets, when fewer fruits and arthropods are available. The beak of the Tooth-bill is particularly adapted to eating leaves, enabling it to tear, manipulate, and masticate pieces of leaves and leaf stems; Figure 2.12. The notched cutting edges of the beak are used to bite or tear and then to fold leaf pieces into a

2.11 A Spotted Bowerbird feeds upon the buds of a eucalyptus tree, Charters Towers, Queensland.

tight wad prior to mastication and the functional cusps, which fit perfectly into indentations on the other mandible, are then used in a chewing action to enhance foliage digestibility by crushing and grinding. During winter Tooth-bills live silently in the forest canopy. They fly little during this period, and eat mainly leaves. As a result of their foliovorous diet, Tooth-bills produce compact faecal 'pellets' that consist of finely-masticated foliage, looking like green tea leaves. With the return of spring and summer, when fruits again become abundant, Tooth-bills revert to a mostly frugivorous diet. Satin Bowerbirds also eat more foliage during winter and masticate leaf matter before ingesting it, but have only slightly notched bills. Satins often graze upon grasses, clover and other herbaceous plants, particularly during winter flocking when other foods are in short supply; Figure 2.13; see Chapter 7.

Arthropods, mostly insects, form a significant part of adult and nestling

2.12 A calling young male Tooth-billed Bowerbird, aged by its pale mouth, shows the 'teeth' on both cutting edges of his beak, Paluma Range, north Queensland.

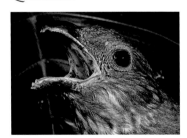

bowerbird diets, especially during their display and breeding periods. Insects eaten include grasshoppers and their relatives, cicadas, mantids, stick insects, beetles, caterpillars, ants, and cockroaches. Flying termites are caught during their nuptial eruptions, and worms, frogs, skinks, and pieces of birds and eggs are also included in the diet of some species. Some arthropods are obtained by snatching, sallying, or are taken in the air by hawking but others are searched for or gleaned from live and dead foliage, tree branches and trunks, epiphytic plants, flowers, and forest floor leaf litter. Black-eared Catbirds also predate the nest contents of small birds and pigeons to feed to their nestlings. Nestling diets are detailed and discussed in Chapter 4.

2.13 Satin Bowerbirds often feed on the ground, upon grass and other plant leaves, Lamington, Queensland.

2.14 Nestling grey bowerbirds, in this case Spotted Bowerbirds, are fed grasshoppers; Charters Towers, Queensland.

Sharing food resources

During display and breeding seasons one to several individuals of a bowerbird species might forage in the canopy of single fruiting trees. This occurs in fig trees, which produce prodigious crops that often ripen simultaneously over a short period of time; Figures 2.2 and 2.5. Black-eared Catbirds, Tooth-billed, Golden, and Satin Bowerbirds live together in tropical rainforests and Green Catbirds, Regent, and Satin Bowerbirds do so in subtropical rainforests. These two groups of species share the food resources available to them in such a way that competition is limited to the extent that they coexist. Fruit choice is the most important factor in permitting these species to live together in the same habitat. They also avoid direct competition by feeding at differing forest levels and situations, in addition to selecting fruits of different suites of plants and different animal types. Additional factors including body size, physical adaptations affecting foraging, size of fruit able to swallowed, the extent of other foods taken like nectar and leaves, also play a part in resource sharing between co-existing bowerbird species.

Diet and mating systems

The dispersion of suitable fruiting trees within habitats is of great significance to understanding differences between monogamous breeding by catbirds on the one hand and the polygynous breeding bowerbirds on the other. Studies of both tropical and subtropical rainforest catbirds show that fig fruits, notably larger ones, form a significant component of both adult and nestling diets; see Chapters 4 and 7. Figs are low in nutritional value but are rich in carbohydrates and plants ripen over relatively brief periods. Individual fig plants fruit asynchronously, so that ripe crops are somewhere abundant throughout the year, including winters when fruits of relatively few other plant species are available. Because fig trees are evenly dispersed throughout catbird habitats, and present their fruit crops in a spatially and temporally predictable way, they provide a viable ecological basis for the territory-based socially monogamous pair bonding of catbirds. Both Green and Black-eared Catbirds cache or store fruits, notably larger figs, about their defended territories, this possibly enabling their females to spend more time near their nests. Cache sites are numerous and include crevices in tree trunks and boughs, in debris between tree forks, and atop epiphytic ferns. Catbirds storing figs in protected places may also enhance the dispersion of food plants, in addition to their defecating seeds about their territories. Thus, catbirds are primary dispersers of figs, within their home ranges.

Unlike the catbirds, the polygynous bowerbirds mainly eat the highly nutritional drupaceous fruits of a great diversity of plants that produce crops that ripen over a longer period than do figs and that are less evenly dispersed, or more clumped, through habitats. Thus, in marked contrast to figs, most of these fruits are economically undefendable because of their spatial and temporal unpredictability. In other words, the exclusive all-purpose territoriality of catbirds could not work for the primarily fruit eating polygynous bowerbird species; because while an area defended by them might contain a fruiting tree(s) during one week or month it could include none the next week or month.

Seasonal abundance of rainforest fruits apparently permits court or bower owning male bowerbirds to be emancipated from nesting duties. Thus males spend inordinate periods of time advertising, attending, defending, and displaying at their traditionally sited court or bower while females nest-build, incubate, and provision their offspring alone; see Chapters 3 and 4. The highly traditional nature of court and bower sites might bring about a local abundance of food plants as seeds defecated by bowerbirds at and about them germination; Figure 2.15. As traditional sites pass from one generation of long-lived males to the next such a local abundance of food plants would enable males to spend more time at their bowers, attracting females and deterring rival males. Similarly, females might nest close to such traditional bower sites because the locally abundant food plants support the provisioning of their offspring.

Males of several polygynous bowerbird species, including at least Macgregor's, Golden, and Great, store fruits about their bowers, Figure 2.16, to be eaten at some future time. Male bowerbirds do not leave their bower exclusively to harvest a fruit to store. Rather they return from a foraging bout with fruit carried in the beak that is surplus to their immediate needs. Storing of fruits may function to maximise time males spend at their bower site, and this is significant to them given the potential for visits by females and by rival males seeking to damage bowers and steal decorations.

Fruits cached in this way are often forgotten by the bird and thus germinate where stored. One female Golden Bowerbird, nesting nowhere near a bower, once left her nest and eggs to fly directly to a nearby liana stem to pick out and

2.15 Many fruit seeds defaecated onto their courts by male Tooth-billed Bowerbirds will germinate there, Paluma Range, north Queensland.

eat a fruit; her sudden and purposeful behaviour suggesting that she knew of the fruit's presence, having previously stored it there. Bowerbirds are not known to digest seeds and are therefore not considered seed 'predators', unlike many parrots and pigeons. To the contrary, bowerbirds are important seed dispersers.

Home ranges

Most bowerbird absences from courts, bowers, and nests are spent in foraging. Distances travelled for food varies both from year to year and at different times of the year depending upon food availability. Aside from foraging, bowerbirds leave their bowers and nests to go to water. They visit creeks, pools, dams and water-filled tree holes to drink and bathe; Figures 2.17 and 2.18. They also drink water droplets from forest floor leaf litter and wet foliage about their bower sites. Other such 'maintenance' activities that are performed by both males and females include preening, anting, and sunning; Figure 2.19. Within their defended all-purpose territory the above activities are the only ones the pairs of socially monogamous catbirds need concern themselves with. Home ranges of Australian catbirds average one to two hectares, but their territory during the breeding season becomes smaller as parents focus their foraging activities closer to their nest. But for both sexes of the polygynous bowerbird species life is far more complicated.

2.16 A bunch of wild pepper fruits, *Piper novae-hollandiae*, stored by a male Golden Bowerbird near his bower for future consumption, Paluma Range, north Queensland.

Activities of males away from their bowers

While court or bower owning adult male bowerbirds aggressively defend their bower sites, little aggressive interaction occurs between them away from bowers as they feed about their home ranges. The home ranges of adult male Macgregor's Bowerbird in New Guinea are approximately 150 to 200 metres in diameter and are generally elliptical in shape, with the bower usually at its centre. In Australia the home ranges of four adjacent court-owning adult male Tooth-bills averaged 9.5 hectares during a display season, with a mean overlap between them of 50 percent. The year-round home range of eight traditional bower site owning adult male Golden Bowerbirds averaged seven hectares. These figures are interesting inasmuch as they show that male Golden and Macgregor's Bowerbirds travel much further from their bowers than Tooth-bills travel from their courts. Clearly this is a reflection of the marked difference in the kind of dispersion of traditional display sites: bowers of Golden and Macgregor's Bowerbirds being evenly and sparsely dispersed whereas Tooth-bills' courts occur closer together and are clumped into aggregations, known as exploded leks, in which males are in vocal but not visual contact; see Chapter 3.

Home ranges of adult males may vary during different times of the year: For example, Satin Bowerbirds in rainforests and woodlands mostly forage within 50 metres of their bowers during the display and breeding season but in winter, when they flock and change their diet to the plant leaves, they travel further as males, up to 40 in a single flock, and female-plumaged individuals. Smaller flocks might consist mostly of a single sex.

2.17 A Spotted Bowerbird drinking, Charters Towers, Queensland.

2.18 A Spotted Bowerbird bathes, as Squatter Pigeons drink, Charters Towers, Queensland.

2.19 Four Regent Bowerbirds sunning themselves, Lamington, Queensland. By and courtesy of Simon Nevill.

Little is known about home ranges of immature males. Young males, wearing female-like plumage, move extensively about their habitat for some five to six years before establishing or acquiring a traditional bower site. As they approach maturity they limit their travels to only several adjacent traditional bower sites before then concentrating on one that they then challenge the occupying adult male for the ownership of. For example, from five to two years before attaining traditional bower ownership, immature male Golden Bowerbirds visit many bower sites, at an average of just under 400 metres from the one they eventually come to occupy. The year before attaining full bower site occupancy this average distance diminishes to some 200 metres. Young males also build and attend rudimentary bowers until they are able to take over a traditional one.

The promiscuous males leave their court or bower sites in order to collect bower materials and decorations, steal them from rival neighbours' sites, or to chase off rivals and destroy their bowers. Adult males direct most of their marauding raids at the bowers of immediately adjacent rivals; Figures 2.20 and 2.21. Adult males also regularly raid the rudimentary bowers of younger males in order to destroy them and steal decorations from them, and younger males will raid those of adults.

Because females select a mate from several immediately adjacent males, neighbouring rival males are clearly any individual male's most direct competitors. The loss of even a small percentage of decorations, to theft by rivals, may represent the difference between mating success and failure to an individual male; see below. Females of the polygynous species also travel around extensively in order to locate males at their bowers, compare them, and select a suitable mate from among them.

Activities of females away from nests

Female bowerbirds maintain relatively large, overlapping, year round home ranges. In one study area the foraging home ranges of female Satins varied from six to 26 hectares over three consecutive nesting seasons, such variation presumably reflecting at least fluctuations in the relative availability of food. Female Satins travelled less than 50 metres from their active nests for 32 percent of their foraging trips, from 51 to 100 metres for 53 percent, and to more than 100 metres for the remainder.

Before or after commencing nest building each season female bowerbirds move freely about their habitat from bower to bower to assess the quantity and quality of bower structures and decorations before selecting a mate. Females must be extremely discerning in whom they permit to father their offspring, because the only contribution the male will make to offspring production is his sperm. Given the lengthy and costly investment that females must make in their progeny they must seek to maximise the quality of genes passed to their offspring by the father. This should at least insure that they have done their best

2.20 A male Spotted Bowerbird about to leave a rival's bower with a stolen decoration, having just destroyed the bower walls, Charters Towers, Queensland.

to enhance the possibility of their sons being relatively successful in the all-important mating game.

Female Satin Bowerbirds choose a mate by a complex process of elimination, during which they make sequential decisions based on male traits, including bower, decoration, plumage, display and vocalisation quality. One study showed that each female's home range included an average of five to seven different males' bowers. Each female samples several of these males and their bowers, initially a larger number and subsequently a smaller one. The individual male found most attractive is then returned to for mating. A female that chooses the most attractive of potential mates in one season typically returns to sample that mate of the previous season in the next year. In being thus faithful by mating with the same, most attractive, male as in their previous season females reduce time spent in mate searching. Thus females quickly improve their mate choice skills.

At some point in her annual mate searching activities a female is stimulated to mate with a particular male by a combination of his bower, decoration, and paint features as well as his appearance, vigour, age, vocalizations, levels of bower attendance, and courtship traits. Males that better clear or build and decorate their bower undoubtedly enjoy greater mating success than males that do so in an inferior way. By this means has the evolution of not only ornate plumages and complex and highly ritualised courtship displays and vocalisations, including mimicry, come about in bowerbirds but also the all but incredible suite of behaviour that is expressed in bower building, decorating, and painting. The clearing, construction, decoration, and painting of a court or bower requires strength, dexterity and acquired skill. The retention of them in good order requires costly investment in time and there is, therefore, potentially much information about the quality, experience, and survival of males available for females to assess. Females preferentially seek older, more experienced, males. Older male Satins certainly do secure more plural matings,

2.21 An adult male Regent Bowerbird surveys the decorations on a Satin Bowerbird's bower with a view to stealing some, Lamington, Queensland.

females clearly selecting the older males to be mated by. Higher numbers of blue parrot feathers, snail shells, or yellow leaves decorating a Satin Bowerbird's bower significantly correlate with greater male mating success, with snail shell numbers explaining the greatest variation associated with success.

A female at a male's court or bower can make some assessment of his fitness by examining the symmetry and quality of bower shape and construction and the relative abundance of decoration types she favours. She can even do this in his absence! The relative abundance of decorations enables females to assess the quality (fitness) of individual males, based upon their success in conflict with rival males; see above. Results of some recent research suggest that females of some species select males that use bower decorations that are rare in nature. Some rare decorations can include most surprising items; Figure 2.22; see Chapters 3 and 6. Females also use the vocalisations produced by courting males, and notably their mimicry, in their choice of mates. The quality of mimicry produced by males probably enables females to assess male age and survival.

The bottom line is that it is the power of sexual selection, by highly discerning females, which dictates that male bowerbirds must make themselves attractive in complex way to enable females to measure the relative genetic fitness of the males. This involves the exercise of notable memory, not only by the females but also by the males in convincing their opposite sex that they are the best. A recent finding, that has much excited both the scientific and semi-scientific media, is that bowerbirds have larger brains than do ecologically similar songbirds of the same body size and faunal region. Moreover, those species building more complex bowers have larger brains than do species building less complex ones. This begs the question can selective mate choice by females result in smarter males? How males perform at their bower site in order to attract and seduce the highly discerning females that travel around their home ranges assessing them is the basis of the next chapter.

2.22 An adult male northern Satin Bowerbird includes the skull of a Musky Rat-kangaroo, *Hypsiprymnodon moschatus*, among his rarer bower decorations, Atherton Tablelands, north Queensland (over page)

3

Bowerbirds at courts and bowers

The highly traditional court and bower sites of male bowerbirds are focal points that most social activities, of adult and immature males and visiting females, revolve around. As discussed in the previous chapter, females of polygynous bowerbird species visit a number of courts or bowers of different individual males in order to be able to base their final choice of mate upon that males' suite of characters. Activities of resident male site owners involve vocalising, bower building, decorating and painting, chasing rivals away, displaying with or without another bird present, courting, and mating. Field studies of seven species (Tooth-bill, Macgregor's, Archbold's, Golden, Regent, Satin and Spotted Bowerbirds) form the basis of this chapter and have made this much clear, but almost nothing is known of the other species.

Courts and bowers are not placed at random within habitats, but are located on favoured topography within an environment that includes one or more characteristics required by males. These might involve appropriate saplings, perches, light conditions, foliage cover and so on. The dispersion of traditional courts and bowers is known for one or more populations of 14 bowerbird species, and details appear in Chapter 7. In all bower-building species adequately known, the traditional bower sites of individual adult males are evenly dispersed through suitable habitat, the fairly constant distances between them being maintained by competitive interactions. What is known is adequate to broadly demonstrate that the more open the habitat of a bowerbird species the more sparsely dispersed are the bowers of males.

The single exception to what appears to be bower site dispersion resulting from male-male competitive social interaction is the clumping of courts by Tooth-billed Bowerbirds. Tooth-bills are exceptional in that their traditional courts average only 50 to 70 metres apart, and at their greatest density may be less than 50 metres apart. Moreover these courts are not evenly dispersed, but tend to be clumped and thus to form aggregations that are termed 'leks'. At these leks the male Tooth-bills are usually not in visual contact from their individual courts, as are males of birds that form true leks, but they are in vocal contact and so their lek is defined as being an 'exploded' one.

Site tenure

The immediate location of a court or a bower is referred to as its 'site'. Courts and bowers are recleared or rebuilt on the same spot as they occurred during the previous season or their location changed to a different spot within the same site. Sites are traditional, in persisting for years, or rudimentary in that they rarely persist for more than one season. Traditional court and bower sites, and in some cases a bower structure itself, are occupied by subsequent generations of males. They become known to generations of locally resident bowerbirds of both sexes and of all ages.

Traditional sites involve a court or bower being regularly attended, maintained, and decorated at a specific location over consecutive seasons, by an individual adult male or by consecutive male owners. Court sites of Tooth-billed, and bower sites of Macgregor's, Archbold's, Golden, Satin, and grey Bowerbirds, have been known to persist for at least one to two, and even more than three, decades. A traditional site may be unused for one or two seasons, after the loss of a long-term owner, only to be subsequently used again when another adult male acquires it. Traditional sites are rarely abandoned. Male Tooth-billed Bowerbirds must, perforce, re-clear their leaf-litter-covered court site each season and, more often than not, they do so on precisely the same spot of rainforest floor.

Whilst a traditional site is consistently used for years the court or bower may be replaced at different locations within the site. For example Golden Bowerbirds studied by us replaced a bower at an average of 14 metres from the previously actively used structure, due to structural deterioration of the original bower. Disused bowers, of former seasons, of Great Bowerbirds and some other grey bowerbirds may persist for years – sometimes resulting in the remains of 10 or more structures persisting beneath a single tree or bush. Once males acquire adult plumage and a traditional bower site they exhibit extremely high fidelity to the latter. Bowerbirds enjoy long survivorship, see Chapter 1, and adult males therefore show long-term fidelity to one traditional court or bower site of up to two or more decades or, in the case of some maypole bower builders, a specific traditional bower structure. Some individual male Tooth-billed, Golden, and Satin Bowerbirds are known to have occupied a particular court or bower site for more than 20 years. Why then are court and bower sites so traditional, and why do males exercise such fidelity of tenure?

A male bowerbird, or successive generations of them, retain a court or bower at a traditional site over years because this repeated use confers advantages in maintaining status within a local population of competing males and encourages repeat visits by locally experienced females. An individual male's time and energy investments in his bower site and bower are considerable. It is likely that male Tooth-bills holding traditional court sites at the heart of an aggregation of courts within the lek are older individuals enjoying higher mating success than their peripheral rivals. Thus advantages to male Tooth-bills in taking over a longer-term and centrally-located traditional court site would be the likelihood of improved status and of females returning to the site of previously successful courtships. Once any male bowerbird has established site occupancy he can ill-afford to be deterred from attending and defending such a hard-won asset to his potential reproductive success.

Young male bowerbirds must enter the established society of court or bower owning peers if they are to have any significant opportunity of reproducing. A pre-existing traditionally owned site is newly occupied as a result of a male replacing or competitively displacing the previous resident. Female-plumaged immature males have an 'apprenticeship' of five to six years spent visiting rudimentary, or practice, courts or bowers of their own making, as well as bowers of older males. During this period they gain experience of bower attendance, building, decorating, painting, displaying, and vocalising. Rudimentary court or bower sites are established by the clearing or construction of a sub-standard, poorly maintained, and inadequately decorated court or bower by one or more immature males, near to traditional sites of older males. Attendance at such a rudimentary site by immature males is sporadic during one to two, rarely more, seasons. Rudimentary sites are abandoned when an attending immature male, usually once he has attained adult plumage, gets to occupy an adjacent traditional site.

Given that adult males are aggressive about their own sites, the establishment of rudimentary sites near them emphasizes their importance to younger males in being able to eventually occupy a traditional site. The inferior nature of rudimentary courts and structures reflects the relatively young age, inexperience, and lack of social dominance of their attending males. This scenario, involving apprenticeship-like activity by younger males, is consistent with the notion that females may preferentially seek out older, more experienced, males; see Chapter 2.

3.1 A Tooth-billed Bowerbird's court, Paluma Range, north Queensland.

71

Courts and bowers

The **court** of the Tooth-billed Bowerbird is not a bower because it is not constructed but is merely an area of ground cleared of debris. The court encompasses the trunk of at least one small tree, this 'display tree' being an essential feature of each court. The court is decorated with larger leaves laid paler side uppermost to contrast them against the exposed soil; Figure 3.1.

3.2 The authors inspect a large, traditional, maypole bower of Macgregor's Bowerbird, Tari valley slopes, Papua New Guinea.

There are two basic structural bower types - the **maypoles** of the gardener-Archbold's-Golden group and the **avenues** of the silky-Satin-grey bowerbird group. The maypole builders accumulate countless orchid stems or sticks and stack them about a vertical sapling or tree fern trunk, or upon horizontal perches. Beneath the maypole or bower perches is a laid out bower 'mat' made of mosses, rootlets, or fern fronds, the Golden Bowerbird excepted. This mat is decorated with piles of specific items; see *Court and bower decorations* below. Bowers of the maypole building species – the gardeners, Archbold's and the Golden - are individually more variable in size, design, and materials. Maypole bowers vary between the four species of gardener bowerbirds. In Macgregor's Bowerbird it is a simple tower of sticks supported by a central sapling or treefern trunk upon a circular mossy base or elevated bowl; Figure 3.2. It is similarly simple in the Onin Peninsula population of the Vogelkop Bowerbird and the Yellow-fronted Bowerbird of Papua, but in these the basal mat is not elevated. More complex diminutive roofed huts or 'tepees' thatched with orchid stems, sticks, or ferns, are built by Steaked Bowerbirds and the Vogelkop and Wandamen Peninsula populations of the Vogelkop Bowerbird; Figures 3.3 and 3.4.

Vogelkop Bowerbirds were long thought to occur only in the mountains of the Vogelkop and Wandaman Peninsulas, where they build complex roofed maypole bowers. As recently as the 1980s additional populations were discovered in the Kumawa and Fakfak Mountains of the Onin Peninsula: Here they build simplistic maypole bowers, fundamentally like those of Macgregor's and the Yellow-fronted Bowerbirds. Following this surprising discovery it was found that an isolated population of Macgregor's Bowerbird, on the Huon Peninsula of Papua New Guinea, builds bowers different to those elsewhere.

The bower style of any particular bowerbird species is partly learned by individuals, and the significant geographic variation in bower structure observed, notably in geographically isolated populations of Macgregor's and Vogelkop Bowerbirds, is a reflection of culturally-transmitted behaviour; see *Court and bower decorations* below. That there is conspicuous geographical variation in bower form in these two bowerbirds would appear to indicate sexual selection for these traits by their females. The odd Macgregor's bower consists of two adjacent towers and bower mats and while these may reflect no more than an excess of building behaviour on the part of individual males they do demonstrate the potential for striking variation in bower form; see Chapter 7.

Archbold's bower is an amorphous structure up to three metres or more high and can occupy an enormous surface area and volume; Golden Bowerbird's bowers consist of one or two substantial towers of sticks that are usually terrestrial and may up be two metres high; Figure 6.14.

The avenue bower type consists of two walls of sticks or grass stems placed parallel and near vertically into a foundation mat of sticks or grasses laid upon the ground, as typified by that of the Satin Bowerbird; Figure 3.7. Bowers of the silky bowerbirds are small, frail, and sparsely decorated avenues while those of the Satin, Spotted, and Great are increasingly larger, stronger,

3.3 A typical roofed maypole
bower of the Streaked Bowerbird,
Kagi, Owen Stanley Range,
Papua New Guinea (right).

3.4 A typical roofed maypole
bower of the Vogelkop
Bowerbird, Arfak Montains,
Papua (below). By and courtesy
of Nancy Woodman.

3.5 While bowers of Archbold's Bowerbirds are an amorphous mass of orchid-draped perches above a mat of fern fronds, as inspected here by Clifford Frith, they are of the maypole type of bower, Tari Gap, Papua New Guinea (left).

3.6 A typical twin-towered maypole bower of the Golden Bowerbird, being examined by Dawn Frith, Paluma Range, north Queensland (below).

and more decorated respectively. A few, aberrant, bowers of Satin and grey bowerbirds have a third or fourth wall added; see Chapter 7. These odd bowers have involved a male building another wall in order to reorientate his avenue alignment only to have failed to remove the original wall; see below. Other such multi-walled structures indicate excessive building activity by the over-zealous owning male, or by an intruding male(s).

In the Fawn-breasted Bowerbird the basic avenue bower is enhanced by it being built upon a raised, and sometimes substantial, basal platform of sticks; Figure 3.8. In Lauterbach's Bowerbird the fundamental avenue is elaborated beyond being built upon a basal platform, by the addition of two substantial end walls built at right angles to those of the central avenue. This results in a box-like structure; Figure 3.9. For more detailed descriptions of the court and the various bowers of the polygynous bowerbird species see Chapter 7.

Bower age

Traditional bower structures of gardener bowerbirds can last a long time, one Macgregor's bower doing so for more than 20 years. Many male Archbold's Bowerbirds renovate and add to their bowers of the last season at the start of the next, on the very same patch of forest floor and perches, one being so used for at least six consecutive years. Some bowers of Golden Bowerbirds persist for more than 20 years, the average minimum life of a bower structure being almost 10 years. Bowers of Satin and grey bowerbirds are refurbished and reused or replaced at their traditional sites annually. One study showed that, in marked contrast, two-thirds of Regents' bowers were maintained for less than 11 days and only five percent of them for more than 26 days. This situation is thought to exist because if intruding male Regents do not destroy the bowers of rivals then their owners, having become aware of the discovery of their bower by a rival, typically destroy or abandon it.

Bower building, orientation and painting

The time it takes to build a complete bower depends upon the size and complexity of the structure - a male Satin builds one within a few hours but a Golden takes one or more seasons to do so. In building males simply drop a stick or orchid stem onto a branch or bower, as in Archbold's, Golden, Vogelkop Bowerbirds, or place a stick or a stem into the ground as in the avenue builders, or on to the structure as in the maypole builders, with a shaking of the head and bill that forces it in place. They do not in any way weave their bower materials; Figure 3.10. The avenue walls of some species are typically aligned to a particular compass orientation, usually north-south. This enhances the illumination of bower decorations and male courtship display, as viewed by a female from within the bower avenue. Bowers of other avenue building species are not typically orientated in a particular direction or are not sufficiently well known for us to be sure; for more details see Chapter 7. More knowledge of where

3.7 The simple avenue bower of a Satin Bowerbird, Atherton Tableland, north Queensland.

3.8 The avenue bowers of Fawn-breasted Bowerbirds are built atop a substantial stick base, Iron Range, north Queensland.

3.9 The most complex of the avenue bowers is that of Lauterbach's Bowerbird, viewed here from above, Baiyer River, Papua New Guinea.

males place their decorations, and how they display relative to the position of the sun, the female, and other factors, are required for a better understanding of bower orientation.

Males of some, if not all, avenue building bowerbirds produce and apply a paint, of charcoal and vegetable matter masticated and mixed with saliva, to the sticks of their bower walls. In applying their paint Satin and some grey bowerbirds sometimes use a piece of vegetable matter as a 'brush'. As a result they are included in the short list of animals that use tools; Figure 3.11. In fact a piece of fibrous tree bark, dry grass stem or such like, is masticated into a small pellet and this, held entirely within the beak, acts as a kind of sponge, wedge, or stopper rather than as a brush to apply paint. Nevertheless if it used to control the flow or application of paint it does act as a tool. The paint stains inner avenue walls at about the standing bird's head height, Figure 3.12, and dries to a dark powdery deposit. Sometimes an intruding male Satin even paints the bower of a rival male!

That painting is an activity that males of several avenue builders invest considerable time in doing raises the question of how it functions. Several functions have been suggested, but no really satisfactory one: Perhaps it

3.10 An adult male Yellow-fronted Bowerbird adds a stick to his simple maypole bower, Foja Mountains, Papua. By and courtesy of Bruce M. Beehler.

provides other bowerbirds with a visual or olfactory means of identifying the individual painter. Freshly applied paint may, however, function to assure females that a bower is actively maintained; and the extent of fresh paint may provide females with an indication of male bower attendance levels. Certainly visiting females will closely examine and pick at or appear to taste painted bower sticks. Bower painting of a kind is alluded to in Macgregor's and Vogelkop bowerbirds but this requires further study and documentation.

Court and bower decorations

While males of some bowerbird species use but one or few kinds of bower decorations, as in the Regent, those of most use several to numerous kinds. Such decorative items may be present in numbers greater than five to ten thousand on a bower. Numbers of decorations enable females to assess individual male quality or fitness based upon their relative success in conflict because males steal decorations from one another; see Chapter 2. Males of each species show clear discrimination for objects of certain size, shape, texture, or colour as decorations. Only leaves are used to decorate courts of Tooth-bills; Figure 3.1. Among other things, leaves are also used as decorations by several maypole and

3.11 An adult male Fawn-Breasted Bowerbird paints his bower wall by holding fibrous vegetation in his beak as an aid to paint application, Silver Plains, north Queensland.

avenue bower builders. Other polygynous species decorate their bowers with a broad array of natural and man-made objects. Decorations used by rainforest-dwelling bowerbirds include flowers, fruits, fungi, lichens, seedpods, insect frass, insects and their skeletons, feathers, bones, and mammal skulls. The grey bowerbirds favour paler decorations such as bones, stones, shells, glass, and moulted external skeletons of cicada nymphs; Figure 3.13.

Different decorations on a bower might perform different functions. For example white bones, shells, and other larger objects may provide distantly visible indicators of a bowers location to females, while small and less striking items function during more intimate male-female courtship interactions at the bower. Objects placed extensively on a bower, such as white bones and shells, could possibly also enhance immediate lighting conditions, by reflecting light, to illuminate the bower, other decorations, or the displaying male.

The placement of decorations on bowers varies between species, and is characteristic of each, but inevitably with some individual variation. Gardener bowerbirds decorate their bower mat and the mossy maypole column base, and some hang insect frass from the ends of lower maypole sticks; see Chapter 7. Decorations are often placed upon the bower mat in discrete aggregations, while some are located on perches above the bower. Similarly, males of grey bowerbirds do lay certain items in discrete piles on particular parts of the bower or about it. Regent, and perhaps other silky, bowerbirds put decorations almost exclusively within their bower avenue whereas Satins place them only on the platforms outside their avenue. Males of at least Macgregor's and Golden Bowerbirds place or cache the odd bower decoration about their bower site, in addition to on their bower; see also Chapter 2.

3.12 An adult male Satin Bowerbird applies paint to sticks of his bower wall, Atherton Tablelands, north Queensland.

Males show great discrimination in where and how their decorations should appear on their bowers; Figures 3.11 and 3.14. Decorations that are displaced upon or are added to a bower, such as by interfering ornithologists, are removed or returned to their proper place immediately upon the return of the bower owner. While it is possible to broadly list the types of decorations typically used as bower decorations by any particular species, many objects of appropriate size, weight, and colour can be adopted, no matter how novel or artificial. For details of bower decorations, their colour, and placement on bowers; see Chapter 7.

Some favoured bower decorations are rare in the birds' natural environment. Satin and other bowerbirds use blue bower decorations and blue is a rare colour in natural habitats; Figure 3.15. It is suggested that male Satins use blue to enhance their own blue plumage but the fact that males of other species, that are not blue, use blue decorations weakens this idea. In addition to their colour, the use of blue parrot feathers by the Satin and of the blue plumes of adult male birds of paradise by Vogelkop and Archbold's Bowerbirds provide examples of the use of items that are undoubtedly rare in the environment; Figure 3.16 and Chapter 6.

A greater abundance of some such favoured, rare, decorations on

3.13 This male Great Bowerbird specialises in large sun-bleached snail shells as bower decorations, Granite Gorge, north Queensland.

a bower is known to improve the mating success of the bower owner. For example, the bowers of gardener bowerbirds on the Fakfak Mountains of Papua have white limestone rocks on them. Such stones are otherwise found only in wells and as water is particularly scarce there these stones represent items that are uncommon and that birds would have to travel far to obtain. Similarly, water-washed pebbles are notable among the decorations of several other bowerbird species, often on bowers far from water. As these stones are heavy for the male birds that must find and transport them their presence on bowers possibly indicates to females something about the strength and vigour of the bower-owning males with an abundance of them.

3.14 Male Golden Bowerbirds place their beard lichen bower decoration in specific places on their bowers, Paluma Range, north Queensland.

Decorations most favoured by one population of male Satins studied were darker blue and reflected higher levels of ultraviolet light than did less favoured ones. These features increased visual contrast between decorations and the substrate they are placed upon and/or between the different kinds of decorations. Given that birds' perception of ultraviolet light is very different to that of humans, sophisticated contemporary studies seek to understand the significance of bower decorations from the bowerbird's point of view.

A lone male Spotted Bowerbird found itself well beyond his own species range, perhaps having been blown there by a storm, but within that of a population of Satin Bowerbirds. He then built a bower and decorated it with

3.15 An adult male Satin Bowerbird at his bower with his most valued of rare decorations – a parrot's tail feather, Atherton Tablelands, north Queensland.

3.16 Adult male Archbold's Bowerbirds decorate their bowers with rare King of Saxony Bird of paradise plumes in order to impress females of their own kind, Tari Gap, Papua New Guinea.

blue items just as male Satins typically do but Spotteds certainly do not. His blue decorations were stolen by male Satins and were in turn retrieved from their bowers by him. This demonstrates the influence of imitative learning, as the Spotted Bowerbird concerned quickly 'changed his spots' in learning to decorate his bower not as his own kind does but as his new found peers and rivals did. Interestingly, the behaviour of this Spotted bird indicates that bower decorations are not necessarily exclusively the direct result of female preference; Figure 3.17.

While each bowerbird species shows a tendency to use the same kinds of natural objects as bower decorations some geographical variation in taste is known in several species: For example in Townsville a Great Bowerbird's bower in a cemetery had marble chips and artificial flowers taken from graves, Figure 3.18; a bower on the university campus had pens, paper clips, and other stationary; a bower within an army barracks had spent firearm cartridges and other military accoutrements; and a bower beside a council workshop area had an abundance of green plastic hinge-pins from garbage bins.

Two geographically isolated populations of the Vogelkop Bowerbird, see *Courts and bowers* above, not only build quite different forms of bowers but they also use different bower decoration types and colours. Onin Peninsula males use drab items and reject colourful ones, while males on the Vogelkop and Wandamen Peninsulas use colourful decorations and ignore drab ones. Thus geographically varying bower styles might be a culturally transmitted trait, as in human art styles. Differing 'cultures' are far more conspicuous with respect to preferred bower decorations between populations of a species than are differences in bower form.

Male bower attendance and activities

Adult male bowerbirds are presumably able to spend inordinate amounts of time at their court or bowers because food resources, particularly fruits, are abundant during their mating seasons. The amount of daylight they spend doing so averages from about 40 to 70 percent, depending on whether the species is primarily fruit or animal eating. Information regarding levels of attendance by males during the months of courtship display is limited to a few species; see Chapter 7.

The most common behaviour of adult males during the reproductive season is perching within or adjacent to their court or bower and advertisement singing; Figure 3.19. As their court or bower and decorations, and time invested in the building and attendance of them, are to attract and impress mates it is important that males effectively advertise their location. This the males of most species do by vocalizing at the court or bower site, which in addition to advertising their presence may also indicate levels of time investment in bower attendance. Tooth-bills spend more than 90 percent of daylight at the court site singing - far more than other bowerbirds spend doing.

Aside from vocalising, a male's time at his site in the absence of females is

3.17 'Billy" the Spotted Bowerbird, having found himself within a population of Satin Bowerbirds, decorated his bower with blue items as Satin Bowerbirds typically do but Spotted Bowerbirds do not. By Jack D. Waterhouse and permission of the Australian Museum.

3.18 The decorations of a Great Bowerbird with his bower built within a cemetary included many items taken from the graves, Townsville, Queensland.

largely spent in maintenance, by adding bower material or decorations, adjusting decoration positions, painting, displaying alone, or deterring and chasing rival males. Periods of time that males of some species spend in performing such activities appear in Chapter 7. Males also often perch silently above their sites preening and, occasionally, feeding. In the presence of a female at his court or bower a male becomes preoccupied with courting her. Male Tooth-bills roost above their courts at night but it remains to be seen if this is true of males of bower attending species. As males are taken by birds of prey, such as goshawks, they perform anti-predator 'frozen' postures at or near bowers to avoid detection; see Chapter 7.

Advertisement song and vocal mimicry

Males advertise their court or bower site with advertisement song and other calls, including mimicry of the calls of other bird species and other sounds of their environment, from habitually used perches. A drawback to frequent vocal site advertisement is that a lack of it will indicate to rival males that the owner is absent and thus provide a window of opportunity for a raid; see *Theft and destruction* below. Advertisment calls consist of variable far-carrying harsh, jarring, churring, chugging, rattling, or deep and hollow whistled notes. Exceptions are the typical advertisement call of male Satins, which is a briefly whistled clear song, and the distinctive prolonged *rattle* of male Golden Bowerbirds.

Males of polygynous bowerbirds also perform vocal mimicry during courtship and upon seeing a potential predator, as do females at their nests. Such mimicry involves the calls of other bird species, but also of other environmental sounds; see Chapter 7. There is little doubt that all polygynous bowerbirds

3.19 Adult males of the recently rediscoverd Yellow-fronted Bowerbird spend much time perched above their bower, Foja Mountains, Papua. By and courtesy of Bruce M. Beehler.

are competent vocal mimics, as at least Tooth-billed, Macgregor's, Streaked, Vogelkop, Archbold's, Golden, Regent, Satin, and all grey bowerbirds are confirmed to do so. Vocal mimicry is fundamentally acquired by learning and can be passed on culturally. Relative age of males would appear to play a significant role in this, as both the repertoire and quality of mimicry improves with age. Among competing Satins, older males produced longer bouts of higher-quality mimicry than younger males and as a consequence gained higher mating success. In producing high quality mimicry during courtship, male Tooth-bills and Satins repeat a repertoire of the calls of other bird species in a specific order. Thus males must remember both the bird calls and the order in which they are to be produced, as must the females that preferentially select those males performing this mimicry well and in the preferred order. It appears clear, then, that sexual selection by females acts upon mimicry to improve male song repertoire and quality; see Chapter 2. Mimicry can be opportunistic, and we have observed male bowerbirds immediately mimicking the call of another species in response to hearing, or even merely seeing, one. Catbirds have not been heard to mimic, at or away from nests.

Theft and destruction

Often apparently in response to the lack of calls from a neighbouring rival's court or bower, a male bowerbird will fly to the unattended adjacent site to damage the bower or steal decorations. Damage is minor to comprehensive, the intruding male grasping a section of bower wall at its base and tearing it out of the ground; Figure 2.19. Males more often visit bowers of rivals only to steal favoured decorations. These actions clearly represent a mechanism by which males directly affect the court or bower quality of rivals, in the eyes of females, and thus their reproductive success. They are mostly directed at sites of immediately neighbouring, and therefore the most important of sexually competing, rivals.

Movements of leaf decorations between nine adjacent traditional Tooth-bill courts, at which we had individually marked the male owners, suggested a social hierarchy at work: That one individual male stole more leaves from more adjacent courts than did all other birds combined, as well as apparently inhibiting all other males from stealing from him, is indicative of a social system similar to that in other bowerbirds. Leaf theft probably results in few, probably the older, males retaining the largest and best-decorated court during each season. Such males presumably obtain most matings, as do those male Satins with more decorations than their peers.

While male Goldens steal the odd recently placed stick from the apex of rivals' bowers, they do not attempt to damage bowers because the action of a fungus, in fusing component sticks together, significantly strengthens their bowers. Nearly all thefts among Goldens are by males of immediately adjacent bowers, although a few individuals do travel further afield; see Chapter 2.

In extraordinary circumstances the males of one bowerbird species will visit the bowers of males of another species in order to steal decorations that are attractive to both: This is known to occur, for example, between Spotted and Great Bowerbirds and between Regent and Satin Bowerbirds; Figures 1.20 and 3.20.

3.20 A male Spotted Bowerbird, in foreground, contemplates stealing decorations from the bower of a Great Bowerbird in his presence, Charters Towers, Queensland.

Courtship displays

Males of polygynous bowerbirds typically display to females by performing highly ritualised postures and movements accompanied by highly specific body, head, and wing movements. A reasonable to good amount is known of courtship behaviour in 12 of the 17 polygynous bowerbird species. For illustrated details of courtship displays of some polygynous species see Chapter 7. Courtship in most of these bowerbirds is instigated by the arrival of a female at the court or bower site, having been attracted by the owning male and his vocalizations. The arrival of a female often results in the attending male immediately moving away from her, as do grey bowerbirds, and hiding from her view as in Tooth-billed, gardener, and Golden Bowerbirds. Hiding may also, or only, feature as a latter part of courtship, as in the avenue builders. While male Tooth-bills and Goldens hide behind trees, male gardener and avenue builders use parts of their bowers to hide behind. Initial Regent, and possibly other silky bowerbird species, courtship is unusual because males advertise their bower location from the forest canopy, with colourful plumage and calls, and then lead females down to the bower.

In most species the male commences his displays on the ground, but in the gardeners some simplistic flight displays between adjacent vertical saplings are sometimes performed first. Uniquely, male Goldens follow initial display posturing by extensive flight and hover displays, followed by hiding behind trees. During this courtship hiding, males typically produce a continuous soft subsong that incorporates vocal mimicry. While being courted, females observe the male passively and silently from a perch, the court, bower mat or bower perch, or from within the bower avenue. In addition to using the bower to hide behind, or interpose between themselves and a female, males use decorations as display 'props': These they hold in the bill or toss toward the female. Latter parts of the courtship of some bowerbirds are aggressive, as males approach females, often resulting in females fleeing temporarily or permanently. Males

3.21 Adult male Yellow-fronted bowerbirds make up for their simplistic maypole bower with an extensive bright crest. This male hides from a female just to the right of his bower, Foja Mountains, Papua. By and courtersy of Bruce M. Beehler.

3.22 Crestless adult male Vogelkop Bowerbirds make up for their drab, female-like, appearance by elaborately decorating a complex roofed maypole bower, Mokwam, Arfak Mountains, Papua (below). By Will Betz.

also often display in the absence of females, when display appears to be directed at the bower and decorations.

Having been suitably impressed by a male's courtship a female makes her readiness to mate clear by solicitation posturing that involves crouching, raising the hindquarters and tail, and drooping vibrating wings. Mating takes place on the court or bower. Immediately following copulation females vigorously and rapidly flutter and shuffle their partly opened drooped wings, but it is not known if this has a specific signal or physiological function such as enhancing sperm movement. Males usually aggressively expel females from their court or bower immediately after mating with them. Rival adult and immature males sometimes interrupt the courtship or mating of a male at his court or bower!

Adult male grey bowerbirds direct a highly ritualised nape presentation posture at females as a latter part of their courtship. Intriguingly, this posture is performed by both the crested Spotted, Western and Great Bowerbirds and the entirely crestless Lauterbach's and Fawn-breasted species. Thus, the crestless species perform a posture designed to present a colourful crest that they no longer wear, but presumably used to wear in their evolutionary past. As these species lost their crest they simultaneously evolved more complex bower structures and decoration to compensate. A similar situation to this grey bowerbird one also occurs within the four gardener bowerbirds: Adult male Macgregor's and Yellow-fronted Bowerbirds wear large colourful crests and build relatively simple bowers compared to the far larger and more complex bowers of the much smaller-crested Streaked and entirely uncrested Vogelkop Bowerbirds; Figure 3.21 and 3.22. Presumably this correlation between relative crest size versus bower complexity, termed the 'transferral effect', occurred as a result of sexual selection by females for meaningful, externalised, symbols of male fitness, bowers and decorations, on one hand and natural selection acting to reduce bright plumage that might attract predators to colourful males on the other hand. Thus courts and bowers, or at least some aspects of them, represent male fitness and replace elaborate male plumage.

As male courtship postures, choreography, and vocalizations are typically stereotyped in presentation and content, are complex and lengthy, and are observed intently by females who often reject males, they must provide important clues to the relative fitness of the performing males. Males must gain experience if they are to impress females with their displays and, to this end, young males will visit bowers of their elders; Figure 3.23. A female having selected the male of her choice and been fertilised then departs the court or bower to attend her nest, eggs, and offspring. The nesting biology of the bowerbirds is comprehensively detailed in the next chapter.

3.23 An immature male Regent Bowerbird, identified by his pale bill and eye, and moulted cicada skin in his bill, displays to another immature male in his bower, Lamington, Queensland (over page).

4

Bowerbirds at nests

The nesting biology of bowerbirds is of great interest because both monogamous and polygynous mating systems occur within the family: And yet these remained all-but unknown until recent decades. Both monogamous and polygynous bowerbird species lay small clutches of one to three eggs, laid at two-day intervals. They have long incubation and nestling periods for songbirds of their sizes and post-fledging periods are extensive, and thus improve juvenile survival rates. These are features typical of the reproduction of some, but not all, 'old endemic' Australian perching birds of Gondwanan origin of which the bowerbirds belong; see Chapter 1.

Both sexes of the catbirds share in the defence of an all-purpose territory. Male catbirds do not assist with nest building, the incubation of eggs, or the brooding of nestlings but they do assist in the feeding of their offspring to their independence. Catbirds feed both fruits, including a high proportion of figs, and animal foods to their nestlings.

All of the other 17 bowerbird species reproduce polygynously. Food resources, mainly fruit, are seasonally sufficiently abundant to permit their males to spend inordinate time at their courts or bowers to attract and court potential mates, and for females to provision their offspring alone. These females invest a great deal of time and energy in nest building, the formation and incubation of their eggs, feeding their nestlings, and the care of their offspring after they leave the nest until they are able to fend for themselves. Thus females must expose themselves to far greater costs and risks than do males in reproducing their kind and, as noted before, the best they can do to maximise their genetic fitness is to select mates that appear to offer greater reproductive benefits.

The start and duration of seasonal egg laying is correlated with relative abundance of food, which varies year-to-year. Nesting seasonality of New Guinea forest bowerbirds is poorly known. This is partly because of the great range of climatic regimes over that island of extensive altitudinal zones. In contrast, the grey bowerbirds of open drier habitats have a protracted breeding season, active nesting occurring through most to all months of the year.

In Australian tropical and subtropical rainforests bowerbird nesting begins during the latter part of the dry season of late August and September, when temperatures, rainfall, and availability of fruit and invertebrates start increasing. The monogamous catbirds usually start nesting in late August or in September and the polygynous bowerbirds in September or late October-November. Egg-laying peaks during October-December, as annual temperatures reach their warmest with the onset of seasonal rain and when fruits and arthropods, particularly

4.1 An adult Black-eared Catbird at its nest with nestling, in Yellow Lawyer Cane *Calamus moti*, Paluma Range, north Queensland.

4.2 A female Tooth-billed Bowerbird incubating on her sparse and frail small nest, Paluma Range, north Queensland.

4.3 A female Macgregor's Bowerbird at her nest and nestling in a pandanus tree crown; food carried to her young is held in her bill and mouth, Tari Valley slopes, Papua New Guinea.

4.4 A female Golden Bowerbird sits tightly on her nest while incubating her eggs, Paluma Range, north Queensland.

4.5 Nest and egg of Archbold's Bowerbird, Tari Gap, Papua New Guinea.

4.6 Nest and eggs of a northern Satin Bowerbird, near Paluma Range, north Queensland.

4.7 Nest and egg of a Lauterbach's Bowerbird, Baiyer River, Papua New Guinea.

locusts, cicadas, and beetles, are at or near their seasonal peak abundance. Wet season rains of January to March bring an end to most bowerbird courtship and nesting, with young leaving nests immediately before or during the early wet season. The peak nesting months for Australian grey bowerbirds precede annual tropical monsoonal rains, during October to December or January, but this varies from year to year. Initial rains bring about a greater abundance of insects, mainly grasshoppers, that stimulate nesting in grey bowerbirds because they represent a large proportion of their nestlings' diets. Hatching of their eggs coincides with the peak seasonal availability of larger insects.

Intensive studies of nesting Green and Black-eared Catbirds, Golden, Regent, and Satin Bowerbirds in Australia and Archbold's Bowerbird in New Guinea provide the basis for this chapter. Limited information is also available for the Tooth-billed, Spotted, and Great Bowerbirds, but little is known of other New Guinea species. Circumstantial evidence from individually banded female Satins shows that they are capable of mating and nesting at two years old, but female age at first breeding is unknown for other species. Mating takes place before or after nest building and up to a month prior to egg-laying. While this chapter deals with bowerbird nesting biology as a whole details of various aspects of it for each species are in Chapter 7.

Nest sites and nests

Bowerbirds often habitually use the same location to build their nest each year, often resulting in an accumulation of used nest structures. Species studied nest solitarily, and it is unlikely that any nest gregariously. Most active nests are within human hearing of a male calling at his court or bower. Bowerbirds typically nest in cryptic sites away from 'pathways' convenient for potential tree climbing predators of eggs and nestlings such as rats, possums, goannas and snakes. Thus nests are sometimes remote from surrounding vegetation, typically in isolated small trees, that would provide access to climbing mammals, or are built within protective dense foliage. For example, Black-eared Catbirds often build nests in the forest understorey among protectively spiny lawyer cane vine; Figure 4.1. Forking branches in trees and bushes are the favoured nest sites for females of most polygynous bowerbirds, but there are exceptions. Female Tooth-bills mostly nest within canopy vine tangles that may be pendant or covering horizontal tree limbs, and sometimes among dense canopy foliage; Figure 4.2. Macgregor's Bowerbird primarily nests within the spiny leathery frond bases of *Pandanus* trees and, uniquely within its family, the Golden Bowerbird builds its nest in tree crevices or between tree buttresses; Figures 4.3 and 4.4.

Catbird nests are large, bulky, deep, open bowl-shaped structures, Figure 4.1, consisting of four basic parts – a sparse to substantial foundation of large sticks that supports the lower nest cup, a deep nest cup mostly of large green or dried leaves, a layer of pieces of decaying wood and/or mud atop the central leafy bowl, and an inner cup lining of fine twiglets and vine tendrils.

Nests of Archbold's, the gardeners, and the Golden Bowerbird are substantial, deep, bowl-shaped structures consisting of three basic parts – a stick foundation, a nest cup mainly of dried leaves and fronds, and a nest cup lining of fine twiglets, rootlets and/or vine tendrils; Figures 4.3, 4.5 and 4.9. Archbold's nests are bulky and larger than those of other species.

Tooth-billed, Regent, and Satin Bowerbird nests are relatively small, frail, shallow, slightly concave, and saucer-shaped, consisting of two parts – a loosely-built outer foundation of dried sticks and an eggcup lining of finer material. In the Tooth-bill the inner lining comprises of fine dry twigs, in the Regent fine dry twigs sometimes with some leaves, and in the somewhat sturdier Satin nest typically with dried *Eucalyptus* and *Acacia* leaves; Figure 4.6. Nests of grey bowerbirds are structurally similar to those of the Regent and Satin, but sticks of the lower foundation are often larger, longer, and more haphazardly placed. Also sticks of the upper nest foundation provide support beneath and around the discrete eggcup lining; Figures 4.7. Dried grasses are typically used for this lining, save in the Great Bowerbird that mostly uses fine twigs and sometimes includes a few leaves typically of *Eucalyptus* or *Acacia* trees. Western Bowerbirds may incorporate *Casuarina* 'needles' into the nest lining. Lauterbach's and Fawn-breasted Bowerbirds sometimes add bark strips to their nest cup and foundation.

Female Black-eared Catbirds take two to three weeks to construct their first nest of the season. Golden Bowerbirds take three to four weeks to nest build. Nest building by Satins and Regents lasts about one to two weeks, and that of Satins typically precedes mating. Whilst most Black-eared Catbird and Golden Bowerbird nests have eggs laid in them within two weeks of nest completion, some are not laid in for four weeks after it.

Eggs and incubation

The catbirds have an average clutch size of one egg in New Guinea and two in Australia. In New Guinea, six polygynous bowerbird species have an average clutch size of one egg and eight species in Australia a clutch size of almost two eggs. Thus clutch size averages markedly smaller in New Guinea than in Australia in both monogamous and polygynous bowerbirds. Australian catbirds tend to lay more three egg clutches than polygynous species but even within the relatively stable environment of tropical rainforest there is year-to-year variation in clutch size. During particularly dry years, when food is sparse, average clutch size is smaller than in climatically normal years.

Bowerbird eggs are elliptical ovate, or long oval, in shape; Figure 4.8. Eggs of the, denser rainforest nesting, catbirds, Tooth-billed, Archbold's, gardener, and Golden Bowerbirds are pale and unmarked. Those of more sparsely foliaged forest and woodland to arid open habitat nesting silky, Satin, and grey bowerbirds are more pigmented and are vermiculated, streaked, or blotched. Because only the female parent attends the nest their eggs must

4.8 A clutch of Great Bowerbird eggs, Townsville, Queensland.

4.9 Nest and clutch of white egg of the Golden Bowerbird, Paluma Range, north Queensland.

4.10 Black-eared Catbird pipping egg and hatchling, near Paluma Range, north Queensland.

remain exposed to view during their absences. The white eggs of the Golden are unique among bowerbirds and their total lack of colour could be an adaptation to their crevice nesting; Figure 4.9. White eggs are typical of crevice and hole nesting birds in general, their paleness making them more visible and thus less likely to be accidentally damaged by parents in their dark nest sites.

The time interval between the laying of successive eggs of a clutch is 20 to 24 hours for the majority of perching birds. Interestingly, bowerbirds lay the eggs of a clutch on alternate days, with their incubation usually starting upon completion of the clutch. The advantages, if any, of two day laying intervals are unknown but perhaps a longer laying interval makes it physiologically possible for a female to lay larger eggs, which may improve growth and survival of the resultant young.

Bowerbirds' incubation periods are notably long, as they are in several other Australasian songbirds. Incubation is solely by the female in both the pairing catbirds and all polygnous species. Females of all of the latter species wear drab plumage, as an adaptation to their unaided nest attendance. Incubation periods are known for only six species in the wild, see Chapter 7; those of female Black-eared and Green Catbirds range from 22 to 24 days, those of Golden, Satin and Great from 21 to 23 days but that of Archbold's, living in a much colder and wetter habitat, is 26 to 27 days. Most parent birds generally spend 60 to 80 percent of the day incubating their eggs, whether only the female or both sexes, and the seven bowerbird species for which information is available fall

4.11 An adult Green Catbird attends its nest and nestling, Lamington, Queensland. By Glen Threlfo.

within this range. Hatching of clutches of more than one egg is synchronous, the siblings emerging within 24 hours of each other; Figure 4.10.

Nestlings

Nestling periods are known for eight bowerbird species in the wild and are long for tropical perching birds. Nestling periods, like their incubation periods, are similar in both monogamous and polygynous species with the exception of Archbold's Bowerbird. The nestling period, being from the day of hatching of the last egg of the clutch until the last young leaves the nest, is 20-21 days for Australian catbirds but 17 to 21 days for polygynous bowerbirds, excluding Archbold's with an average of 30 days. Archbold's long nestling period is all the more notable because its females have only single nestlings to raise. This presumably reflects adaptation to a cold and wet high altitude habitat, where insects are sparse.

Nestling care in catbirds involves only the female brooding them, but both parents attend to their food, hygiene, and protection; Figure 4.11. In polygynous species only females perform nesting duties; Figures 4.12 to 4.16. Time spent brooding by the female parent appears to be affected by brood size as both Black-eared Catbirds and Golden Bowerbirds spend more time brooding single nestling broods than larger ones, presumably because smaller broods are less demanding or because siblings stay warmer longer than do lone nestlings. The point at which bowerbirds cease brooding nestlings varies from species to species. Parents swallow their nestlings' faeces throughout most of the nestling period and only when nestling development is advanced do they carry faecal sacs and seeds voided into the nest by nestlings away; Figure 4.16.

4.12 The only image known to the authors of a female Vogelkop Bowerbird attending her nest, and nestling, Arfak Mountains, Papua. By and courtesy of Adrian Forsyth.

Nestling diet

Bowerbirds feed nestlings of all ages both fruits and animals, mostly insects. A nestling meal usually consists of one or several fruits of a plant species or one kind of animal prey. Parents carry food along the length of their bill and in their mouth. Only rarely are two fruits of different plant species, two different animal species, or both fruit and animal species, delivered as a single meal. The proportion of fruit in the nestling diet is similar for the two Australian catbirds, averaging more than 70 percent, but the relative proportion of fruits and animals fed to nestlings varies between the polygynous species. Like the catbird pairs, female Archbold's and Goldens feed more than 70 percent fruit to nestlings, but Satins and Regents feed less than 35 percent fruit. The proportion of fruit in nestling diets of grey bowerbirds is only slightly less than that of animals, and that of fruit in Black-eared Catbird and Golden Bowerbird nestlings' diets increases with nestling age.

4.13 A female Archbold's Bowerbird on her nest containing a well-developed older nestling, Tari Gap, Papua New Guinea (opposite above).

4.14 An adult female Regent Bowerbird attends her nest and nestlings, Lamington, Queensland. By Glen Threlfo (opposite below).

4.15 A female Satin Bowerbird attends her nest and newly hatched chick, near Paluma Range, north Queensland (left).

4.16 A female Great Bowerbird takes her nestling's faecal sac to remove it from the nest area, Townsville, Queensland.

Insects are the most important animal foods fed to nestlings. The proportion of them fed is greatest just after hatching and declines thereafter. The assumption is that more arthropods are fed to younger nestlings in order to provide the calcium necessary for their initial bone formation, proteins for tissue, organ, and feather production, and lipids for energy needed for growth. Once nestlings reach a certain age dietary needs can probably be provided by a selection of fruits only, some of which are rich in protein and lipids. Although fruits are relatively nutritionally poor, because of their low protein content, compared to insects most contain sufficient protein to meet the needs of growing nestlings.

While catbird pairs specialize in feeding figs to their offspring the unaided females of polygynous bowerbirds specialise more in feeding a particular type of animal to theirs: Archbold's feed tree-climbing lizards as 30 percent of their nestling animal diet, see Figure 4.17, as well as insects and pieces of other birds. Cicadas represent 55 percent of all animal items fed to Goldens' nestlings'; females catch a cicada and reduce it to pieces near their nest, returning to its remains repeatedly until all is fed to their nestlings. Cicadas also represent a significant component of nestling Regent and Satin diets. Scarab beetles are also important for Satin nestlings. Beetles and cicadas are delivered to Satin nestlings largely intact, but cicadas and other larger insects may have their wings removed before delivery. Butterfly and moth caterpillars represent an important component of diet for advanced Regent nestlings. Grasshoppers and crickets dominate the nestling diet of the Spotted and the Great Bowerbirds to the extent of some 60 and 70 percent of their animal diets respectively. Female grey

4.17 A female Archbold's Bowerbird about to feed her nestling the tail of a tree-climbing lizard, Tari Gap, Papua New Guinea.

bowerbirds usually remove the head, wings, and legs from larger grasshoppers and related insects before feeding them to their young; Figure 4.18.

Nestling growth and development

Hatchling bowerbirds characteristically have pink-orange to yellowish-orange skin, varying shades of yellow to an orange gape, a white egg tooth, and conspicuous long fluffy down; Figure 4.19. Nestlings wear dense long down in patches on the crown, wings, and body; this down being reddish grey-brown in catbirds, greyish-brown in Tooth-bills and gardeners, dark greyish-brown in Archbold's and Golden Bowerbirds, and a much paler grey in Satin, Regent, and grey bowerbirds. Beak and leg colour is variable; for descriptions of nestlings see Chapter 7. The eyes of nestlings start to open when they are about seven to nine days old and are fully open by nine to 12 days of age. Nestling wing flight feathers start to appear at 5-6 days in the Black-eared Catbird and Golden and at 8 days old in Archbold's. The larger wing feathers (primaries) burst from their pin sheaths on days 13-14 in the Black-eared Catbird and 11-12 in the Golden, but not until 14-15 in Archbold's.

Nestlings leave the nest when well feathered, in a plumage broadly similar to that of their parents, but with a tail of less than 10 percent of the average length of their parents. Down persists at some feather tips until briefly after nestlings leave the nest; Figures 4.14 and 4.19 to 4.22. What little is known about juvenile bowerbirds suggests there is a long period of dependency upon their parent or parents, lasting at least 40 to 60 days after they leave the nest;

see Figures 4.21 and 4.22. Little is known about what foods are fed to juveniles; Figure 4.25.

Parental behaviour at nest sites

Upon becoming aware of a potential predator, nesting females of several species will perform a 'frozen' posture to avoid detection. When discerned by a potential predator a parent will often perform a 'distraction' display, produce vocal mimicry, or attack or chase the intruder. Parents of both Australian catbirds will repeatedly perform distraction displays near their nests, but not mimicry. Such defensive displays involve an initially vocal parent fluttering to the ground and performing a slow open-wing-fluttering, stumbling, crawl over forest floor. A second catbird parent often perches nearby giving typically harsh scold notes. Female Tooth-billed, Archbold's, Golden and grey Bowerbirds with large young in the nest also perform a distraction display, typically on the ground, while vocally scolding the intruder.

Neither Archbold's nor Golden females have given vocal mimicry when

4.18 A female Great Bowerbird feeding a cleaned grasshopper body to her nestling, Townsville, Queensland.

confronted by the authors at active nests. However, mimicry of the calls of predatory birds given by females, apparently as nest defence, is known in Satin, Fawn-breasted, Spotted, Western, and Great Bowerbirds. Calls of other, non-predatory, birds are also given under such circumstances as well as mimicry of non-avian sounds. Female Spotted, Western, and Great Bowerbirds give a remarkably cat-like meowing near their active nests, as do males at their bowers.

Instances of females mimicking the calls of aggressive and predatory birds near their nests, and by males near their bowers, could be for the ears of the potential predators in order to distract them. Or they could be to attract other birds that might then mob the predatory visitor, as small birds commonly do. Another possibility is that by mimicking the calls of predators as they approach, a female provides her offspring with a predator-specific alarm that the young may then associate with the danger (if surviving the present one). This would potentially increase her fitness, by improving the chances of the survival of her offspring.

4.19 A typically downy bowerbird nestling, this being of the northern Satin Bowerbird, near Paluma Range, north Queensland.

4.20 An advanced Great Bowerbird nestling will shortly leave the nest, Townsville, Queensland.

4.21 Fledgling Black-eared Catbirds that have just left the nest, Paluma Range, north Queensland.

4.22 Fledgling Golden Bowerbirds that have just left the nest, Paluma Range, north Queensland.

4.23 A female Lauterbach's Bowerbird, incubating on her nest in tall grass stems, pants during the heat of the day at Baiyer River, Papua New Guinea.

4.24 A hot and panting female Spotted Bowerbird shades her nestlings from direct sunlight, Charters Towers, Queensland.

Incubating and brooding bowerbirds tend to remain still, to avoid attracting the attention of predators, but do respond to heat and sun by panting, sunning or shading their nestlings; Figures 4.23 and 4.24.

Production of offspring

Bowerbirds nest once a season but may renest following the loss of a clutch or brood, particularly if it occurs early in a season. Given that nest building usually takes one to three weeks, incubation and nestling periods each last about three weeks, and it takes at least two to three months to raise a fledgling to independence, few females could have time to raise a second brood in a single season; Figure 4.25.

Proportions of successful nests, eggs, and nestlings are far greater in catbird pairs than in the polygynous Golden, Regent and Satin Bowerbirds; see Chapter 7. Catbirds produce more fledged offspring than do polygynous bowerbirds, their number of fledglings per nesting being twice that of Goldens and three times that of Satins. It is not surprising to find higher productivity in the large, powerful, and pair-bonding catbirds compared with the polygynous species in which females nest alone. Two adults obviously provide greater protection against nest predators, this alone being an important benefit of biparental care.

Climatic extremes can profoundly affect the nesting success of bowerbirds.

During particularly dry or wet nesting seasons productivity may be reduced, and under the most extreme of climatic conditions no offspring may result from eggs laid. For example, during an exceptionally dry year of our studies that resulted in scarce food resources only five percent of Black-eared Catbird eggs produced fledglings, at a rate of one tenth of a fledgling per parent compared to the normal average of one fledged offspring per nesting pair. In an exceptionally wet January Black-eareds abandoned their broods, which died of exposure, in order to find sufficient foods for their own survival.

Whilst there are many reptile, bird, and mammal species that would take the contents of bowerbirds' nests and the attending adult, records of them actually doing so are few. The causes of bowerbird egg or nestling losses remain largely unknown. Catbirds are themselves not infrequent predators of the nest contents of other birds, including other bowerbirds. Green Catbirds and Satins are also considered predators of Regents' nest contents. These and other predators of nests contents aside, those bowerbirds that have been studied nesting are able to maintain a respectably high level of success in terms of numbers of offspring produced from eggs laid in climatically typical years. Most of the meaningful knowledge summarised above was gained only during recent decades: The next chapter places this into the context of earlier discoveries of basic bowerbird biology.

4.25 A parent White-eared Catbird, with red eyes, accompanies it's juvenile offspring, with grey eyes, to a rainforest pool to drink, Brown River, Papua New Guinea. By Brian J. Coates.

PART II

THE BOWERBIRDS AND PEOPLE

The owner of this Vogelkop Bowerbird's bower near Mokwam, Arfak Mountains, Papua, added novel items as decorations that it obtained from an ornithologist's camp. By Will Betz.

111

5

Bowerbirds discovered

5.1 The Masked was the first bowerbird species found and, being a colourful adult male, it was at the time wrongly thought to be a bird of paradise. From Levaillant's 1801-1806 book (see Further reading).

The trading of bird plumes out of New Guinea, predominantly those of adult male birds of paradise, has gone on for at least two to five thousand years. Initially this was to the eastern Indonesian Archipelago, the Philippines, and the Southeast Asian mainland, but then from the early 1500s until the early 1900s it was also to Europe and subsequently to America. For millennia these extraordinary birds of paradise have served as the centrepiece of myth, ceremony, dress, and dance for a diversity of peoples who have long occupied New Guinea and its neighbouring islands. The people of New Guinea wear bird of paradise, and to far lesser extent bowerbird and other, plumes as decoration even today, and they continue to be traded within that vast mountainous and forest-clad island and beyond it.

The discovery of the first bowerbird species inevitably resulted from the vast plume trade. It is understandable why the first two bowerbird species made known to science, the Masked and the Regent, were not at the time appreciated as being members of an entirely new bird family, that was to become the bowerbirds, Ptilonorhynchidae. For they could hardly have been more spectacularly colourful and thus bird of paradise like in appearance; Figures 5.1 and 5.2.

5.2 The first known image of an adult male Regent Bowerbird, wrongly thought to be a honeyeater at the time, was painted in 1805. By and kind permission of the Natural History Museum, London.

Gold-crowned Honeyeater

5.3 Papuan naturalist I. S. (Saem) Majnep (1948-) and New Zealand anthropologist Dr. Ralph Bulmer (1928-1988) wrote a book about birds of the Kalam area of Papua New Guinea. Permission and courtesy of Fairfax Publishing.

Early collectors

Much of the early trapping and shooting for European collectors and traders was carried out using traditional methods practiced by Papuan and Aboriginal hunters for centuries. Explorer and collector Albert S. Meek wrote in his 1913 book *A Naturalist in Cannibal Land* "To snare Bower-Birds and Birds of Paradise natives search for the playground of the bird, and then set a snare of a loop of native twine in which the bird gets entangled." Macgregor's Bowerbirds were easily trapped at their bowers and sometimes several were taken at the same one. "Hunters may build a cover of tree fern foliage right over the bower, leaving just a small entrance with a springe set in it, and the birds will still come and get caught." wrote Papuan naturalist Saem Majnep; Figure 5.3. Early collectors not only trapped birds but also shot large numbers of them at a single bower or location for museum collections. Papuans used bows and arrows, the latter often blunt-tipped in order to avoid blooding the birds' feathering. Australian Aboriginal people of the Bellenden Ker Range, tropical Queensland, used to catch Golden Bowerbirds by applying a bird 'lime', made from the sap of fig or pine trees to the bird's bower perch.

By the end of the nineteenth century 18 of the 20 bowerbird species were described and the two species remaining undiscovered, the Adelbert and Archbold's Bowerbirds, were to be described in 1929 and 1940 respectively; see page 138. As new bowerbird species were defined and described, from dried skin specimens arriving at scientific institutions about the world from the remote forests of New Guinea and Australia, the desire to find out if any more of them also built such odd and wonderful bower structures grew. Among the first bower structures to be discovered and decribed were those of some grey bowerbirds. In

5.4 Captain, John L. Stokes' (1812-1885) served on H.M.S. *Beagle* before, during, and after Charles Darwin's voyage.

113

5.5 John Gould (1804-1881), the famous English 'bird man'.

5.6 Archibald J. Campbell (1853-1929), prolific Australian ornithologist.

1836 explorer George Grey came across what he thought were 'nests' of kangaroo-rats in northwestern Australia until informed by ornithologist John Gould that they were in fact bowers of the Great Bowerbird. Grey was sufficiently interested to note that water-washed stones had been placed in bowers that were far from both watercourses and coasts. Given the geographical location of Grey at the time, they must indeed have been bowers of the Great Bowerbird.

During Captain John Lort Stokes' November 1839 visit to northern tropical Australia aboard the H.M.S. *Beagle*, the very vessel that carried Charles Darwin on his world voyage during 1831-1836, he found a Great Bowerbird's bower on the Victoria River; Figure 5.4. At that time he thought that an aboriginal mother must surely have built the structure for the amusement of her children. He subsequently described the bower, in 1846, noting that the sticks of the structure had "their tops brought together so as to form a small bower". This description was clearly influenced both by the writing of John Gould, which stimulated great and widespread interest in the building habits of these odd Australian birds in the British public, and the 'arbour' or 'bower' like shape of the structure. Gould not only first called the structures 'bowers' but also observed that they were used primarily for courtship. However, at that time Gould could not know that only males build and regularly attend bowers.

The word bower derives from the word bow, which simply means something that is curved, bent, or arched and thus, for example, the word rainbow. We think that John Gould, Figure 5.5, used the word bower specifically for the short- and arched-walled structure of the Satin Bowerbird, as distinct from the long-walled "avenue", as he termed it, of the Spotted Bowerbird. We conclude that in coining the terms 'bower' and 'bower bird', Gould had in mind the short and arched structure or framework, forming a 'bower' or 'arbour' and often with a seat within, commonly decorating formal English gardens of his time. Indeed, it is probably no coincidence, given Gould's appreciation of the courting function of the birds' structures, that such garden 'bowers' often served specifically as an appropriate place for a couple to meet and become acquainted, or to court; if under the close scrutiny of a chaperone.

The latter part of the nineteenth century was a boom period for professional field collectors seeking birds' nests and eggs for private and institutional collections, especially in Australia. Of 723 clutches of Australian bowerbirds' eggs that we examined in museums around the world, 63 percent were collected between 1878 and 1910, and 83 percent between 1878 and 1930. These figures emphasise the intensity of egg collecting during those periods, particularly by the two famous Australian-born oologists, or students of birds' eggs, Archibald J. Campbell, Figure 5.6, and Alfred J. North, who were then actively, independently and competitively, collecting nests and eggs. These they described prior to including them in their forthcoming books on Australian birds nests and eggs. Campbell's two volume work was published in 1901 and North's superb four volumes during 1904 to 1914.

Mostly due to the efforts of these two men Robert Bowdler Sharpe,

DISCOVERED

Figure 5.7, ornithologist at the Natural History Museum of London, was able to include details of nests and eggs of the Satin, Golden, Regent, Fawn-breasted, Spotted, and Great Bowerbirds in his superb monograph about birds of paradise and bowerbirds, published during 1891 and 1898. The early discovery of these clearly demonstrates the extremes that North, Campbell, and other avid collectors went to in order to be the first to describe the nests and eggs of various bowerbirds. Surprisingly, the nest and eggs of five species formally remain unknown, although those of the Vogelkop Bowerbird were recently photographed in the wild; see page 99 and Chapter 4.

As there was underlying the demand for new specimens a, sometimes all too competitive, desire for novel or new forms a large number of new 'species' were described in relatively short order. As a result confusion occurred with respect to the classification of the various bowerbird species, and some of this took considerable time to appreciate and sort out. The historically important details of discovery and formal description of the various bowerbirds, their bowers, nests, and eggs, and the circumstances and intrigues surrounding them, are discussed below by group; and are summarised on page 138.

5.7 Robert Bowdler Sharpe (1847-1909) of the Natural History Museum, London.

The catbirds

The first catbird, and third bowerbird, species made known to science was the Australian Green Catbird, wrongly thought at the time of 1815 to be a true shrike, of the family Lanidae, by Gustav de Paykull. Descriptions of the White-eared and the Black-eared Catbirds followed, in 1835 and 1858 respectively. Alfred North was the first to describe the Australian Black-eared Catbird nest and eggs, taken on the Atherton Tableland of northeastern Queensland by E. J. Cairn and renowned zoological collector Robert Grant in 1887. The first description of Green Catbird eggs, collected in 1890 in the Tweed River District of New South Wales by W.J. Grime, was also by North and published in 1891. According to North's rival Archibald Campbell these were not, however, the first to be collected and he wrote "The first authenticated finds of Cat Birds' eggs were by Mr. Henry R. Elvery, Richmond River (in 1881), and by my venerable friend Mr. Herman Lau, South Queensland (in 1886). These finds were not reported at the time, and the credit fell to Mr. W. J. Grime...". Campbell published a description of the nest collected by Lau in 1886. The industrious Austrian collector Emil Weiske, Figure 5.8, discovered the nest and eggs of White-eared and Black-eared Catbirds in southeastern New Guinea during his expeditions of 1897 to 1900, and he described them in 1902.

Tooth-billed Bowerbird

Edward Pierson Ramsay, Figure 5.9, described the Tooth-billed Bowerbird, in 1876, from birds shot with a rifle by police Inspector Robert Johnstone near Cardwell on the east coast of north Queensland. Johnstone was the first to describe the simple, leaf decorated, cleared court of the species. The nest

5.8 Emil Weiske (1867-1950) collected birds about tropical north-east Queensland and New Guinea during 1895-1900.

5.9 Dr. Edward P. Ramsay (1842-1916), Australian zoologist and botanist, described many bird species.

and eggs of the Tooth-bill remained unknown when both Campbell's and North's books appeared, but this was soon rectified: During 1908 George Sharp collected a nest and clutch, later described by North in 1909, which the well-known Australian egg collector Sidney Jackson, Figure 5.10 and 5.11, had fervently hoped to be the first person to collect. However, Jackson did publish the first photographs of them in 1909, which he personally discovered and collected.

Gardener bowerbirds

The first gardener bowerbird described was the Vogelkop Bowerbird, in 1871; the Streaked, Macgregor's and Yellow-fronted were described during the next 24 years, see page 138, but the initial discovery and description of these birds were not without considerable confusion!

The Dutch collector C.B.H. Von Rosenberg, Figure 5.12, described the drably plumaged Vogelkop Bowerbird from birds collected in the Arfak Mountains of the Vogelkop Peninsula by Heinrich R. Schlegel in 1871. As no crested Arfak Mountains birds appeared in Europe for more than 20 subsequent years Robert Sharpe, Figure 5.7, was correctly convinced the sexes were similar. Then, in 1895, a fully crested male was described by Adolf B. Meyer, Figure 5.13, curator of birds at the Dresden Museum in Germany, as representing adult males of this species. As a result Sharpe was able to add a figure of this crested male to his illustration of the Vogelkop Bowerbird as his publication went to press; Figure 5.14. Unfortunately, however, the crested male was not taken from the Vogelkop Peninsula. Thus it was not a Vogelkop at all but a Macgregor's Bowerbird that, unbeknown to Sharpe at the time of his writing, was described by Charles W. De Vis, Figure 5.15, curator at the Queensland Museum, Brisbane, in February

5.10 Sidney W. Jackson (1873-1946), Australian bird collector and photographer. Permission and courtesy of the National Library of Australia, Canberra.

5.11 A Sidney Jackson photograph of a Tooth-billed Bowerbird nest and eggs. Permission and courtesy of the National Library of Australia, Canberra.

5.12 German Baron C.B.H. Von Rosenberg (1817-1888) collected in the then East Indies and wrote the book *Reistochten naar de Geelvinkbaai op Nieuw–Guinea in de jaren 1869 en 1870.*

1890! The bird De Vis described was from the Musgrave Range, in what is now Papua New Guinea. Because of this misunderstanding the early bowerbird literature contains several texts and two or more colour plates depicting the male Vogelkop Bowerbird as being colourfully crested, when in fact it is identical to its drably plumaged females; Figure 5.16. In the midst of this confusion Robert Sharpe wrote of Lord Walter Rothschild's collection in England containing "adult males, in nuptial plumage", which is to say fully crested, of gardener bowerbirds from the Arfak and Owen Stanley Mountains of New Guinea; the Owen Stanleys being home to both Macgregor's and Streaked Bowerbirds. This was impossible because only Vogelkop Bowerbirds live in the Arfak Mountains, and its males are drab and crestless; Figure 5.17. The misleading situation arose because people initially thought that birds from eastern New Guinea belonged to the same species as those living on the Vogelkop Peninsula. In fact they were of the species that was to become known as Macgregor's Bowerbird, in which adult males are indeed adorned with an extensive orange crest.

The latter confusion was further compounded within Sharpe's text about the Streaked Bowerbird and its bower: Zoological collector Carl Hunstein first obtained crested adult male Streaked Bowerbirds in 1884 and sold them to the professional collector Otto Finsch. Robert Sharpe in London then described the Streaked Bowerbird as a new species in a scientific journal in 1884. In his subsequent book he then unfortunately repeated a report by Charles De Vis concerning Sir William Macgregor, Figure 5.18, obtaining a male Streaked "in the vicinity of its bower" at an altitude of 4,100 feet on Mount Suckling, and reproduced drawings of the bower concerned from De Vis's report; Figure 5.19. The bower depicted is, however, clearly one of Macgregor's Bowerbird but with an additional

5.13 German Dr. Adolf B. Meyer (1840-1911) wrote *The Birds of the Celebes and Neighbouring Islands* and described several bird species. Courtesy of the Staatliches Museum fur Tierkunde, Dresden.

5.14 An illustration of a crested adult male Macgregor's Bowerbird, at top, that was wrongly attributed to the Vogelkop Bowerbird, and a Yellow-fronted Bowerbird, at bottom, published in Sharpe's Sharpe's *Monograph of the Paradiseidae and Ptilonorhynchidae* of 1891-1898.

5.15 British born curator and director of the Queensland Museum, Brisbane, Charles W. De Vis (1829-1915) named many bird species.

arched 'wall' added to it. The Danish collector A. P. Goodwin first published a description of the distinctively different bower of the Streaked Bowerbird in the same year. Ironically Sharpe notes that A. P. Goodwin's description of the Streaked Bowerbird's bower differs from the erronious De Vis one he quotes! In hindsight we can note that as a male Streaked Bowerbird was shot near the odd bower it is possible that it was attending and adding sticks to the Macgregor's bower. De Vis described the bower of Macgregor's Bowerbird in 1890.

But we must step back a little in time, because it was the Italian explorers and biological collectors Otto Beccari and Luigi M. D'Albertis, Figures 5.20 and 5.21, who first made known to an intrigued world public the amazing bower building and decorating abilities of the New Guinea gardener bowerbirds, in 1877; Figures I.1 and 5.22. They found one of the most impressive of all bower structures, that of the Vogelkop Bowerbird in the forests of the Arfak Mountains of the Vogelkop Peninsula in September 1872 (see Introduction). As the first westerner to behold such constructions Beccari simply could not believe what his Papuan associates told him, that the artistically decorated complex structures were the work of a small bird. Like Captain Stokes, see above, Beccari was led to conclude that they were built and decorated by parents for the amusement of their children.

In the early 1980s American Professor Jared Diamond, Figure 5.23, found that the Vogelkop Bowerbird lives well beyond its previously known range of the mountains of the Vogelkop and Wandamen Peninsulas. He discovered other populations on the Kumawa and Fakfak Mountains of the Onin Peninsula of Papua that builds a bower unlike that built by Vogelkop Bowerbirds elsewhere. Thus while the appearance of adult males is the same, crestless and female-like, throughout the mountain ranges occupied by this bowerbird their maypole bowers and decoration take on two distinctive forms. Those on the Tamrau, Arfak, and Wandammen Mountains being typically hut-like, see Chapter 7, generally like those of Streaked Bowerbirds, while those on the Fakfak and Kumawa Mountains are simple roofless structures generally like those of Macgregor's Bowerbird. That said it does remain to be conclusively proven, by genetic means, that the birds on the Onin Peninsula are in fact Vogelkop Bowerbirds and not a population of a distinct and different bowerbird.

The last of the gardener bowerbirds, the Yellow-fronted Bowerbird, was made known to science by the arrival in Europe of at least three dried adult male skins. These were obtained by collectors operating on behalf of the major plume trader Rennesse van Duivenboden, based on Ternate Island just to the west of Halmahera in the northern Moluccas, of the then Dutch East Indies, now Indonesia, from 1830. This bowerbird only became known at that time because of the extensive brilliant yellow crest of the adult males making them attractive to the plume trade; Figure 5.17. Walter Rothschild purchased these three adult male specimens for his outstanding zoological collections at his Tring Museum in Hertfordshire, England, and he was able to confidently describe them as representing an entirely new species in 1895; see Appendix. Rothschild died

5.16 Adult male, in foreground, and female, in background, Vogelkop Bowerbirds are identically drably plumaged. From John Gould's *The Birds of New Guinea* 1875-1888.

in 1937 and did not live to find out where the lovely Yellow-fronted species lived: Indeed this knowledge was to remain a complete mystery until 1981, see below.

Despite repeated attempts to discover the home and bower of this gorgeous bowerbird, involving at least a dozen expeditions by both professional bird collectors and ornithologists, all efforts failed. It was not until October of 1979 when avid ornithologist and persistently hardy New Guinea explorer Jared Diamond found live birds at several bowers on the remote uninhabited Foja, or Gauttier, Mountains of Papua and he described its simple, Macgregor's Bowerbird-like, maypole bower in 1982. The home of the Yellow-fronted Bowerbird was not again visited by a western scientist until Dr Bruce M. Beehler, Figure 5.24, of Conservation International, Washington, visited the Foja Mountains as leader of his major expedition: During this he made exciting ornithological discoveries and obtained the first photographs of the living bowerbird at its bower in December 2005. Some of his images of the bird appear in this book.

Emil Weiske discovered the nest and eggs of Macgregor's and Streaked Bowerbirds during his expeditions to southeastern New Guinea during 1897 to 1900, and described them in 1902. The nest and egg of the Vogelkop Bowerbird remains to be described formally, but were recently found and photographed by American zoologist Will Betz in May 1991 at Hungku, Anggi Lakes, Papua and also by English biologist David Gibbs near Mokwam in the Arfak Mountains in early October 1994. In 1992 Adrian Forsyth took photographs at a nest containing a well developed nestling; Figure 4.12. The nest and eggs of the Yellow-fronted Bowerbird await discovery.

Archbold's Bowerbird

The last bowerbird species to be made known to science was described in 1940 when Austin L. Rand of America described the distinctive new genus *Archboldia* for Archbold's Bowerbird from the remote western New Guinea highlands. It was named after Richard Archbold, then Research Associate of Mammalogy of the American Museum of Natural History and benefactor of the "Archbold Expeditions" to New Guinea. The bower of Archbold's was first described by Ernst Mayr, Figure 5.25, and E. Thomas Gilliard, curators of ornithology at the American Museum of Natural History, New York, as recently as 1954.

Gilliard collected and studied bowerbirds, birds of paradise, and other birds in New Guinea with enthusiasm and passion; see Prologue and Page 137. In New Guinea in 1950 he employed Papuan hunters and one of them became a wealthy man by the standards of his peers. The latter individual snared two Archbold's Bowerbirds at a bower and traded them to Gilliard who paid for each bird the equivalent of a Papuan's income for a year - a steel axe, two gold-lip shells, a machete, table knife, mirror, and assorted small shells, beads, matches tobacco, salt, and newspaper. So eager was Gilliard to obtain further specimens

5.17 Walter Rothschild's 1896 illustration of a crested male Macgregor's Bowerbird, that he wrongly attributed to the Vogelkop Bowerbird, at top, a male Streaked and, at bottom, two views of the then newly discovered Yellow-fronted Bowerbird (opposite).

5.18 Sir William Macgregor (1846-1919) was Administrator of British New Guinea, where he collected birds.

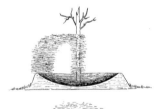

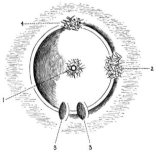

5.19 An odd bower of Macgregor's Bowerbird, reported by Charles De Vis in 1890.

5.20 Italian botanists Dr. Otto Beccari (1843-1920), the first westerner to see a maypole bower.

5.21 Italian Count Luigi D'Albertis (1841-1901) wrote the controversial book *New Guinea: What I did and What I saw.*

5.22 An adaptation of the illustration of a Vogelkop Bowerbird's bower, published by Otto Beccari during 1877-78 (see title page and Introduction).

of what he thought to be a new bowerbird species that he offered a similar reward for every further specimen anyone brought him. To his amazement only the man that snared the original two birds managed to obtain any more – nine of them, all trapped at a single bower! Gilliard asked this man to take him to the bower but the latter was, understandably, most reluctant to make his veritable 'gold mine' known to anyone else. He did eventually lead Gilliard to the bower, but no doubt for a further princely sum.

The eagerly awaited discovery of Archbold's nest and eggs did not occur until 1987, when we found them in the Tari Gap of the Southern Highlands of Papua New Guinea, and described them in the scientific literature the following year.

Golden Bowerbird

The classification of the Golden Bowerbird was, like that of some of its close relatives the gardener bowerbirds, subjected to unfortunate confusion. This involved a problem common to many species in which females differ strikingly from males discovered one sex at a time during early ornithological classification. This particular instance was more unusual, however, as only one ornithologist was involved. In 1883 Charles De Vis, curator at the Queensland Museum named a new genus and species of bird *Prionodura newtoniana,* after the eminent British ornithologist Alfred Newton. It was, De Vis wrote, an unsexed bird showing a "plentiful lack of beauty" which he possibly recognised

as a bowerbird in that he considered it an "aberrant form" of the bird of paradise family. Kendall Broadbent had collected this bird in upland rainforest near the headwaters of the Tully River of tropical north Queensland; Figure 5.26.

In March 1889, collector Archibald Meston, Figure 5.27, collected a breathtakingly beautiful golden-plumaged bird on the rainforested heights of the Bellenden-Ker Range, near Cairns, and lodged the specimen with the Queensland Museum. Charles De Vis immediately named this striking new bird as a new genus and species, *Corymbicola mestoni*, in a brief Brisbane newspaper article titled 'A new bird'. Had he waited but a few weeks he would have appreciated that this lovely golden male bird was associated with large stick bowers, for it was then that he received additional specimens and field notes from Kendall Broadbent. As a consequence of this surprising new intelligence De Vis wrote 'A further account of *Prionodura newtoniana*' during the same year and in that publication he accepted that his *Corymbicola mestoni* was the same species as *Prionodura newtoniana* and observed that the appearance of the former was that of females and immature males of the latter. Unfortunately for Archie Meston this enlightenment meant that what in the interim had become known as Meston's Bower Bird was to become Newton's, and subsequently the Golden, Bowerbird. Meston could not accept this loss of his very own bird and, perhaps understandably, steadfastly continued to refer to it in his own writings as Meston's Bower Bird. Charles De Vis described the vast stick bower of the Golden Bowerbird, discovered by Archie Meston in 1889, in that year. Its

5.23 Professor Jared Diamond rediscovered the Yellow-fronted Bowerbird in 1979. By K. David Bishop, courtesy of Jared Diamond.

5.24 Dr. Bruce M. Beehler studied and photographed the Yellow-fronted Bowerbird in 2005 and 2007. By Gustavo Fonseca and courtesy of Bruce M. Beehler.

5.25 Professor Ernst W. Mayr (1904-2004) published prolifically in evolutionary biology and described many new birds, including bowerbirds, from New Guinea. Permission and courtesy of the Ernst Mayr Library of the Museum of Comparative Zoology, Harvard University.

massive proportions and shapes came as a great surprise to ornithologists.

Robert Sharpe included a description of a nest and eggs said to be of the Golden Bowerbird, discovered by Archibald Meston and first described by De Vis in 1889. Meston found the nest "in the fork of a small tree about seven feet from the ground" and noted "The female flew off the nest, and the male was sitting on an adjoining tree." Campbell included De Vis' description of these in his book, even though he considered them to possibly be those of the "Fly-Robin (*Heteromyias*), [now called the Grey-headed Robin] and not of the Golden Bower Bird." He was correct, and the nest and eggs of the Golden and Tooth-billed Bowerbirds remained unknown when both Campbell's and North's books appeared. But this situation was soon rectified: An Aboriginal employed by George Sharp on the Evelyn Tablelands first collected a nest and clutch of the Golden Bowerbird on 9 November 1908. North exhibited these at a meeting of the Linnean Society of New South Wales on 25 November of that year, before describing them in print in 1909.

Silky Bowerbirds

It was from a plume trade skin that Englishman George Edwards, Figure 5.28, painted a Masked Bowerbird in 1750. The illustration appeared as the "Golden Bird of Paradise" illustrated in the 1750 book *Natural History of Birds III* by Edwards; Figure I.2. French naturalist René Lesson, Figure 5.29, who sailed aboard the ship 'Coquille', obtained trade skins of the Masked during his time collecting and trading birds of paradise in the Dorey Bay area of western New Guinea. This bird was formerly described in the literature by the great Swedish taxonomist Carl Linnaeus, Figure 5.30, father of plant and animal classification by his 'binomial' method of using a genus and species name for each organism, as early as 1758. Linnaeus included the bird in question as *Oriolus aureus* in

5.26 Kendall Broadbent (1837-1911) was a taxidermist at the Queensland Museum, and collected birds in that State. Permission and courtesy of the Queensland Museum .

5.27 Archibald Meston (1851-1924) joined Kendall Broadbent on his Mt. Bellenden-Ker expedition. Permission and courtesy of the Cairns Historical Society.

the famous tenth edition of his *Systema naturae per regna tria naturae*. The bird was not in fact an Old World oriole, of the family Oriolidae as the erroneous scientific name implied, but was an adult male Masked Bowerbird.

It is coincidental that the second bowerbird species to be described, 50 years later, was also an adult male of another species of silky bowerbird. This was the Regent Bowerbird of Australia. John W. Lewin, who illustrated it in his *Birds of New Holland* in 1808, described this exquisite bird; Figure 5.31. Interestingly, however, in researching the present book we learnt about a painting of the Regent Bower that pre-dated that description by Lewin. This 1805 painting is by F. Davies and has long been housed in the Natural History Museum in London but remained unpublished until now. William Swainson established the genus *Sericulus* in 1825, alluding to the silken (*serikos* in Greek) plumage of adult males, for what was to become the Regent Bowerbird.

Otto Beccari and Luigi D'Albertis climbed into the Arfak Mountains from Dorey Bay, via Andai village, in 1872 and there found Masked Bowerbirds, previously known only from dried trade skins, living in their habitat. While people of these mountains told D'Albertis that the Masked 'nested' on the ground he did not see a bower, which was clearly what his informants were alluding to. In 1928, both German-born American evolutionist Ernst Mayr and Australian aviculturalist Fred Shaw Mayer, Figure 5.32, were independently shown an avenue bower in the Arfak Mountains. These can only have been bowers of the Masked Bowerbird, which had remained unknown to science for the best part of two centuries after the discovery of the bird that built them. The first description of a bower, albeit but a couple of lines liking it to the bower of the Regent Bowerbird, appeared in Tom Iredale's 1950 book and based upon a letter from Fred Shaw-Mayer. The indefatigable Thomas Gilliard subsequently photographed in colour an adult male Masked at its rather substantial avenue bower in the Tamrau Mountains of western New Guinea.

The relatively modest avenue bower of the Regent Bowerbird was discovered in 1863, and formally described in 1864, some half a century after Lewin described the bird. But a drawing of a Regent Bowerbird's bower had been made on Ash Island on the 22 September 1861, by one of the sisters Harriett and Helena Scott; Figure I.5.

The Flame Bowerbird was discovered on the upper Fly River of New Guinea and described in 1879, but it was not until 1967 that its bower was discovered on the Nomad River of what is now Papua New Guinea and made known to science in 1970 by Australian ornithologist Harry L. Bell, 91 years later; Figure 5.33.

The Adelbert Bowerbird was the penultimate bowerbird species described, by American James Chapin in 1929. This lovely novel new species was discovered by the professional collector Rollo H. Beck who stated, because he did not want competitors knowing where he collected it, that it had come from Madang. As a result it was often referred to as the Madang Bowerbird before it was found to actually live on the Adelbert Range, near Madang. But the bower of

5.28 George Edwards (1694-1773) of England wrote and illustrated bird books.

5.29 René P. Lesson (1749-1849) described many birds.

5.30 Carl Linnaeus (1707-1778) of Sweden was first to name many plants, animals and birds.

this highly distinctive bowerbird remained unknown until as recently as 1986, when our esteemed Australian friends and colleagues Roy Mackay and Brian Coates were led to an active bower on 8 September by Ningowa, a woman of Ilebaguma village. Roy Mackay described and illustrated the bower in 1989.

The first silky bowerbird egg described was that of the Regent. Both Edward P. Ramsay and Alfred North published a description of it, 22 pages apart in the very same journal in 1886! Not to be outdone, Campbell undertook "an excursion to the Richmond River district, New South Wales, with a view to obtaining, amongst other items, the eggs of the Regent Bird." in November 1891. While Campbell observed a female Regent nest-building he was too early to find eggs but a farmer, whose property he had visited, sent him a pair of fresh eggs in late December which he described in 1893. Coincidentally, in 1886 North had described a portion of eggshell found on Ash Island, in the mouth of the Hunter River, in 1861 as being of the Spotted Bowerbird but he later admitted it was "undoubtedly that of a Regent Bower-bird." Had he not made this error he would have pre-dated Campbell in being the first to describe the Regent Bowerbird's egg. The nests and eggs of the Masked, Flame and Adelbert Bowerbirds await discovery in the forests of New Guinea.

Satin Bowerbird

The Satin Bowerbird was erroniously first said to be a new kind of chough, which are members of the crow family Corvidae, by Frenchman Louis J. P. Vieillot in his 1816 *Nouveau Dictionaire d'Histoire Naturelle*; Figure 5.34. In 1820 Heinrich Kuhl erected the genus *Ptilonorhynchus*, alluding to the fact that feathers (*ptilon* in Greek) cover the base of the bill (*rhunkhos* in Greek) for the Satin Bowerbird. The formal discovery of the bower is credited to Charles Coxen, Figure 5.35, brother-in-law of the great ornithologist John Gould. It was a bower Coxen had collected and donated to the then Sydney, now Australian, Museum that Gould was initially amazed by in 1838-1839 and described as a 'bower' for the first time in 1840; see above.

Campbell's 1883 description of an authenticated Satin nest and eggs, collected by Lindsay Clark in that year near the Bass River, Western Port, was the first. Edward Ramsay, then curator of the Australian Museum, published what he thought was the first description of them in 1875 but, as there was doubt about their authenticity, he subsequently described two confirmed clutches in 1887 and thus postdating Campbell's description.

Grey Bowerbirds

The scientific descriptions of the five species of grey bowerbirds spanned some 60 years; see page 138. In 1830 William Jardine and Prideaux Selby initially described the Great Bowerbird as *Ptilonorhynchus nuchalis*, thus demonstrating their appreciation of its close relationship to the Satin for which the genus *Ptilonorhynchus* was established. Captain John Lort Stokes found a Great Bowerbird bower on the Victoria River in November 1839, while visiting

5.31 The first published illustration of a Regent Bowerbird, an adult male, by John W. Lewin (1770-1819); (opposite, see Further reading).

5.32 Fred(erick) W. Shaw Mayer (1899-1989) bird collector and aviculturalist (here with a Pesquet's Parrot) lived in New Guinea where he was known as *Masta Pisin* (birdman). Courtesy of Errol Fuller.

5.33 Australian Lt. Col. Harry L. Bell MSc., PhD. (1929-1984) at a Flame Bowerbird's bower, Nomad River, Papua New Guinea. By R. Garrett, permission of the Australian Army.

5.34 Louis J. P. Vieillot (1748-1831), was a French ornithologist who described many bird species.

5.35 Charles Coxen (1809-1876) collected birds for John Gould and acted as his agent in Australia.

northern tropical Australia aboard the H.M.S. *Beagle* during 1831-1836, which he described in his 1846 book *Discoveries in Australia.*

In 1837 John Gould first named the Spotted Bowerbird, as *Calodera maculata*, in his *Synopsis of the Birds of Australia* but gave it no English name. He described the bower of the Spotted Bowerbird in 1840. John Gould first made known the Fawn-breasted Bowerbird and its bower in 1850. He also identified the Western Bowerbird in 1862. As a result of the Horn Expedition to central Australia, George A. Keartland described the bower of the Western Bowerbird, which is hardy discernable as differing from bowers of the Spotted Bowerbird, in 1896.

Lauterbach's Bowerbird, the last grey bowerbird species made known, was named by Anton Reichenow of Germany in 1897, after the German botanist Carl Lauterbach who discovered the bird the previous year on the Jagei River in the upper Ramu Valley of then German New Guinea and now Papua New Guinea. Its bower was not, however, described until 1948, by the great Australian bird photographer and early bowerbird student Norman Chaffer in the Wahgi Valley of what is now Papua New Guinea; see Figure 6.11. While there is no doubt that bird collectors familiar with this bird, notably Fred Shaw Mayer and Captain Ned Blood, Figure 5.36, must have observed bowers before 1949 no description had been published prior to that of Norman Chaffer.

Because of similarities between Regent and Spotted Bowerbirds' eggs, some confusion exists as to who did find the first eggs of the latter species. Edward Ramsay was, however, the first to formally describe an authenticated clutch of the Spotted, in 1875. Whether the clutch Ramsay described was actually the first discovered remains unconfirmed. Archibald Campbell considered the first Spotted eggs found were in fact those exhibited at the London Zoological Society in 1873. On the other hand North believed that eggs collected near Grafton in September 1864, sent to him by John Macgillivray, Figure 5.37, constituted the first authentic Spotted clutch.

The original Fawn-breasted Bowerbird nest and eggs description was made by North in 1886, based upon material sent to him by Bertie L. Jardine of Cape York, at the extreme north-eastern tip of Australia, and detailed in Sharpe's great monograph. No sooner had Sharpe's work appeared than nests and eggs of two additional grey bowerbird species were discovered: The nest and eggs of the Great were first described by North in 1896.

In October 1898 a Mr. C. E. Cowle found a Western Bowerbird nest with eggshell fragments within it south of Mareena Bluff in Central Australia, and the following year a James F. Field found a nest and eggs near Alice Springs Telegraph Station. The energetic North also first described these, in 1899. An egg described in 1895 by Adolf B. Meyer as that of Lauterbach's Bowerbird was later thought by him to have been that of the Fawn-breasted. It was not until 40 years later, when Norman Chaffer visited the Wahgi Valley at the invitation of Captain Neptune Blood, that the nest and eggs of Lauterbach's Bowerbird were collected, and then described by Chaffer in 1949.

Finely illustrated books on bowerbirds

Once new bowerbirds and their bowers were discovered by science and made known to the public of Victorian Britain, and quickly thereafter by the western world in general, people became enthralled by reports of bowerbirds' bower architecture and the behaviour of the birds at these extraordinary structures through the pages of finely illustrated books.

That bowerbirds began to feature significantly in some of the greatest of fine ninteenth century books ever published is because they were seen as most closely related to, if not actually part of, the bird of paradise family; see Chapter 1. The first of these publications was by the Surinam-born Frenchman François Levaillant, Figure 5.38, published during 1801 to 1806. His book about the birds of paradise includes the Masked Bowerbird; Figure 5.1. Another early work on birds of paradise, that includes details and illustrations of both the Masked and Regent Bowerbirds, was by Frenchman René Lesson, Figure 5.29, published during 1834 to 1835.

The above two books were to be followed by the grand and limited edition large folio volumes that are today eagerly sought by wealthy collectors of fine and rare antiquarian works. The initial tomes are not specifically about the bowerbirds, or the birds of paradise, but are general bird works. John Gould published volume four of his spectacular and highly acclaimed *The Birds of Australia* in 1848, containing beautiful hand-coloured lithographic plates of the Green Catbird, Regent, Satin, Spotted, and Great Bowerbirds: To these he added Rawnsley's Bowerbird, a bird he considered a probable hybrid, and the Fawn-breasted and Western Bowerbirds in a 1869 supplement to that work. Gould

5.37 John Macgillivray (1821-1867) collected birds in Australia and on adjacent islands.

BOWERBIRDS

5.38 François Levaillant (1753-1824), was a French explorer and collector who produced several ornithological works that included bowerbirds.

5.39 Daniel G. Elliot (1835-1915) became Curator of Zoology at The Field Museum. Chicago, USA.

followed this grand publication with his monumental *The Birds of New Guinea and the adjacent Papuan Islands* during 1875 to 1888, co-authored by Robert Sharpe, into which he slipped a number of birds that were not available to him at the time of his writing *The Birds of Australia*. As a result, his book of New Guinea birds includes, superior and more life-like, illustrations of White-eared and Black-eared Catbirds, Streaked, Vogelkop, Tooth-billed, Masked, Spotted, and Great Bowerbirds. Some of these illustrations, together with others, are used to introduce the species accounts of Chapter 7 herein. Next to nothing was known about the nests and eggs, let alone the nesting biology, of any bowerbird when John Gould produced his nineteenth century volumes on the birds of Australia and New Guinea.

The first scientifically significant finely illustrated book dealing with bowerbirds, albeit as members of the bird of paradise family, was New York born American Daniel G. Elliot's, Figure 5.39, impressive *A Monograph of the Paradisaeidae, or Birds of Paradise,* self-published in 1873. This huge double elephant folio volume was illustrated by the two greatest bird artists of the period, Joseph Wolf, Figure 5.40, and Joseph Smit. Elliot's fine book, admirable in both scientific and artistic terms, includes the three catbird species, seven of the polygynous bowerbirds, and a lovely plate of and brief text about the then unique hybrid known as Rawnsley's Bowerbird; see pages 50-51.

Described as a continuation of John Gould's *Birds of New Guinea*, Robert Sharpe's two volume small folio *Monograph of the Paradiseidae, or Birds of Paradise, and Ptilonorhynchidae, or Bower-birds*, appearing during 1891 to 1898, is one of the last and loveliest of all great hand-coloured bird books. The splendid lithographic plates that illustrate it are based upon wonderfully life-like drawings by J.W. Hart, and J.G. Keulemans; Figure 5.41. Volume two includes all three catbirds and 13 of the polygynous bowerbirds. As curator of ornithology at the British Museum Sharpe's text is scientifically significant, but inevitably leans heavily upon the book by Elliot published a couple of decades previously.

Of the hand-coloured lithographic plates depicting bowerbirds in the finer great bird books the vast majority depict typical specimens, and mostly in admirably life-like postures (considering the artists had not seen the birds in life). There are, however, exceptions. For example, in Sharpe's monograph plate 20 of volume two, Figure 5.14, does not show an adult male Vogelkop Bowerbird as is stated, but an adult male Macgregor's Bowerbird. This happened due to confusion over the provenance of some specimens as detailed above. Gregory Mathews, Figure 5.42, was an ardent Australasian ornithological bibliophile. In the last of his own 12 volumes on *The Birds of Australia*, appearing during 1910 to 1927, Mathews illustrated all 10 Australian bowerbirds, but at that time considered the Western a subspecies of the Spotted Bowerbird; Figures 5.43. 5.44 and 5.45. Mathews also pointed out that while the Regent Bowerbird was described and first figured by John Lewin in 1808, an illustration of the species signed by F. Davies and dated 1805 is now housed in The Natural

130

History Museum, London, collection of original drawings, see Figure I.4, and was once the property of John Latham. Latham (1740-1837) was an Englishman who wrote several multi-volume works on birds and is regarded by some as the father of Australian ornithology.

Tom Iredale, Figure 5.42, published his highly idiosyncratic *Birds of Paradise and Bower Birds* in Melbourne in 1950, copiously but ornithologically poorly illustrated by his wife Lilian Medland. Iredale added little to biological knowledge or understanding of the bowerbird species, but as the last species was described in 1949 his book does include all of them.

Of course it was the extremely fine and colourful illustrations, beautifully hand coloured in the earlier publications, which attracted subscribers to books that including various bowerbird species. But these lavishly illustrated books are now rare and valuable, and are unobtainable save by wealthy collectors. Thus in the 1970's three books appeared that were largely designed to fill this void; two being facsimiles with respect to their colour plates and the third containing original work strongly based upon and following the Gould tradition of bird illustration.

In 1977 both a full size bound and a loose-leaf 'folio' facsimile edition of Elliot's monograph, limited to 250 copies, was printed in Holland for an American and Dutch reprint publisher. In 1980 an intriguing tiny 'pocketbook' facsimile edition of the Elliot plates appeared in German, without the original text but with a brief introductory one by Armin Geus. In 1988 a large, slim, soft cover 'precursor edition' of a facsimile of Elliot's monograph, containing 22 of the original plates including those of the Regent, Rawnsley's and Spotted

5.40 Joseph Wolf (1820-1899), a German, was one of the greatest wildlife artists of all time and he painted several bowerbirds.

5.41 J. G. Keulemans (1842-1912) was a fine and prolific Dutch bird artist long based in London. Courtesy of Errol Fuller.

5.42 Australian Gregory M. Mathews (1876-1949) published a great deal about Australian birds, and described numerous bird species, including bowerbirds while ably assisted by Tom Iredale (1880-1972).

Bowerbirds and abridged text, was published in Australia: The complete facsimile, intended for 1989 publication, never appeared.

In 1978 a slim hardback book by Michael Everett, ridiculously titled *The Birds of Paradise,* was published out of New York and London. It was reprinted in 1987 under the more accurate title *The Birds of Paradise and Bowerbirds --* for both printings include 13 plates of bowerbirds. That this ill-conceived and poorly produced book, with its grossly inadequate and frequently inaccurate text, could run to a second printing is testimony to nothing but the demand for illustrations of extraordinarily colourful and attractive birds. The book *The Birds of Paradise and Bower Birds* by Australians Joseph Forshaw and William Cooper was published in 1977, as a "companion volume" to Thomas Gilliard's 1969 fine book inasmuch as it comprehensively illustrated the species, which Gilliard's book did not.

Academic books about bowerbirds

As bowerbirds and their bowers, nests, and eggs, were discovered and made known to science in-depth studies were performed and published about the birds, including serveral academic books; see Further Reading. By the time *The Bower-birds, their Displays and Breeding Cycles* by Australian Professor A.J. (Jock) Marshall, Figure 5.46, of Melbourne's Monash University, was published in 1954 the nests and eggs of 14 species were known. Only limited information about incubation and nestling periods was available, for captive bred Regent and Satin Bowerbirds, however.

Although some earlier field studies first brought to light some of the remarkably unusual behaviour exhibited by the "unbirdlike" bowerbirds several misconceptions arose concerning how and why they do what they do. Many of these are dealt with in Jock Marshall's book, but a few of them have persisted to the present. One of the most widespread misconceptions about Tooth-billed Bowerbirds was brought about as follows: Sidney Jackson observed and photographed several broken snail shells about a stone at the edge of an active Tooth-bill court and therefore assumed that the bowerbird fed upon snails, having broken them on the stone. He did not consider that his find indicated the feeding of an entirely different bird species, probably of the Noisy Pitta that was then well known to feed upon snails in this way. Jackson's erroneous observation led Jock Marshall to state in 1951 that adult Tooth-bills "certainly feed" upon snails: He even suggested that this might have in turn led to Tooth-bills being able to co-exist with Black-eared Catbirds because they ate snails while catbirds do not. Tooth-billed Bowerbirds do not eat snails.

Of some notes made by Fred Shaw Mayer, Marshall wrote in 1954 that they "reveal that the Black [= Archbold's] Bower-bird eats fruits as well as quantities of land-molluscs. The snails are carried to a special stone or fallen tree-trunk where they are broken. A heap of broken shells marks the feeding-place." Shaw-Mayer was quoted as actually writing "A number of shells of land snails were also

5.43 The Black-eared (above) and the Green Catbird (below) illustration from volume 12 of Mathew's *The Birds of Australia* published 1925-1927: On page 132.

5.44 The Regent Bowerbird illustration, adult male above and female below, from volume 12 of Mathew's *The Birds of Australia* published 1925-1927: On page 133.

5.45 The Spotted (above) and Western Bowerbird (below) illustration from volume 12 of Mathew's *The Birds of Australia* published 1925-1927 (opposite).

5.46 Dr. A.J. (Jock) Marshall (1911-1967), founding Professor of Zoology and Comparative Physiology at Monash University, Melbourne wrote the first acadmic book about bowerbirds. Copyright and courtesy of the Royal Australasian Ornithologists Union.

found on the ground." and as this refers to snail shells as bower decorations it hardly justified Marshall's intepretations. These erroneous assertions that Tooth-billed and Archbold's Bowerbirds ate snails, by breaking them upon a stone, led in turn to a speculative suggestion of a correlation between such feeding and some characteristics of bowerbird skull structure. It was even suggested of the bowerbird skull that this, quite imaginary, feeding habit might account for the "specialized features of this family as adaptations for snail eating". This entire story provides an example of how a completely groundless myth enters the literature until accepted as fact to then be subsequently elaborated upon.

Other misconceptions quoted by Marshall but since laid to rest include that the Green Catbird, and subsequently also applied to the Black-eared Catbird, clears and decorates a ground court like Tooth-billed Bowerbirds do. Wild catbirds do not clear courts. Another long-standing error was that the orchid

5.47 Dr. Ernest T. (Tom) Gilliard (1912-1965), Adelbert Bowerbirds in his hands, in New Guinea. He wrote a fine book about bowerbirds and birds of paradise. By kind permission and courtesy of *The Auk*, journal of the American Ornithologists Union.

stems or sticks of gardener bowerbirds' and Golden Bowerbirds' bowers are glued together with saliva and other components by males. While no evidence exists to support this suggestion many observers, including us, have noted that such bower material is fused together by the action of a fungus ubiquitous to the habitat of the bowerbirds concerned.

The next academic book written after that by Marshall was the *Birds of Paradise and Bower Birds* by Thomas Gilliard, Figure 5.47, which appeared in 1969. It contained no descriptions of nests and eggs additional to those in Marshall's book. As a result of his dedicated intellect and energy Gilliard's work remained the definitive synthesis of bowerbird biology for 45 years and was a watershed in advancing knowledge of and interest in, including our own, the birds and their behaviour; see Prologue.

Since Marshall's 1954 and Gilliard's 1969 benchmark publications there has been a dramatic increase in the numbers and intensity of studies of live bowerbirds, especially over the last three decades. This is also true of theoretical considerations of them and their behaviour by biologists based in Australia, the United States of America, the United Kingdom, and Europe. During the 1980s almost 50 scientific publications specifically about the bowerbirds appeared, in the 1990s almost 70 did so, and during only the first six years of the new millennium well over 50 appeared in the literature. While recent research is summarised in our 2004 academic volume *The Bowerbirds – Ptilonorhynchidae* a very great deal remains to be learnt about these remarkable birds. Even today the nest and eggs of some species are still unknown or undescribed; see page 138. The scientific community presently knows precious little about some half of the 20 known bowerbird species.

Ever since the first discovery of the birds and their bowers the considerable popular and scientific literature has struggled with the complex and tricky issues of levels of intelligence and perception among these most amazing of birds. What we do know for certain is that bowerbirds continue to intrigue and fascinate people of all walks of life, in part because of their perceived intelligence, as is detailed in the next chapter.

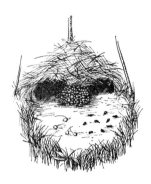

Chronology of the scientific description of bowerbird species, their bowers, and eggs

Common names	Year formally described (published)		
	Bird	Bower	Eggs
Masked Bowerbird	1758	1950	Undescribed
Regent Bowerbird	1808	1864	1886
Green Catbird	1815	-----	1891
Satin Bowerbird	1816	1840	1883
Great Bowerbird	1830	1846	1896
White-eared Catbird	1835	-----	1902
Spotted Bowerbird	1837	1840	1875
Fawn-breasted Bowerbird	1850	1850	1886
Black-eared Catbird	1858	-----	1888
Western Bowerbird	1862	1896	1899
Vogelkop Bowerbird	1871	1877	1994[1]
Tooth-billed Bowerbird	1876	1876	1909
Flame Bowerbird	1879	1970	Undescribed
Golden Bowerbird	1883	1889	1889
Streaked Bowerbird	1884	1890	1902
Macgregor's Bowerbird	1890	1890	1902
Yellow-fronted Bowerbird	1895	1982	Undescribed
Lauterbach's Bowerbird	1897	1948	1949
Adelbert Bowerbird	1929	1989	Undescribed
Archbold's Bowerbird	1940	1954	1988

[1] Discovery date only, no formal description to date

6

Bowerbirds in human culture

The indigenous peoples of New Guinea have been deeply fascinated by the complex bower building and decorating behaviour of male bowerbirds, for perhaps fifty-thousand years or more. Even today the Huli People of the Southern Highlands of Papua New Guinea greatly admire the decorated bowers of Macgregor's and Archbold's Bowerbirds as the work of birds of superior intelligence and industy. They are acutely aware that it is the males that build the bowers and accumulate, and steal from one another, bower decorations; and that they do so to impress and obtain matings with multiple females each season. Papuan men, with the help of their relatives, must accumulate considerable wealth in the form of a 'bride price' before they can take a wife. Given this cultural heritage with respect to obtaining a wife these people relate closely to, and are fascinated and amused by, the birds' apparent dedication to such focused industry, artistry, courtship and procreation.

The first European people to witness bowerbirds' activities at their bowers often referred to these structures as places of play. The notion of early naturalists that bowers are mostly for the birds' amusement persists in the minds of many people to this day. Not that it can be categorically denied that bowerbirds might not enjoy the sight of their bower and decorations. In the chapter *Comparison of the mental powers of Man and the lower animals* of his book *The Descent of Man,* even Charles Darwin could not resist alluding to the bowerbirds under his subtitle *Sense of Beauty;* Figure 6.1. Of them he wrote, "the playing passages of bower-birds are tastefully ornamented with gaily-coloured objects; and this shews that they must receive some kind of pleasure from the sight of such things." We now know that bowerbirds primarily use their bowers for anything but play or amusement, but actually use them for sexual encounters with females and fiercely competitive ones with rival males.

Because of their complex behaviour bowerbirds have always been associated with high intelligence and exceptional artistic abilities, for animals as lowly as birds. Perceptive earlier naturalists thought that bower structures must be associated with courtship of the birds, while the vast majority of writers of the time attributed a strong aesthetic sense to them. Between 1920 and 1950 Australian ornithological literature reflected a strong shift toward the view that, while sexuality is involved, building of bowers and display at them are primarily recreationally and aesthetically motivated. These activities were also often said to be indicative of high intelligence. An academic view is, however, that male bowerbirds behave compulsively and without conscious awareness of the results of their behaviour, as indeed do many people, but this is not to deny

6.1 Charles Darwin (1809-1892), great English gentleman, naturalist, geologist, evolutionist, genius.

6.2 Adult male King of Saxony Birds of Paradise wear two remarkable 'flagged' head plumes (see Figure 6.3), Tari Gap, Papua New Guinea (opposite, top left).

6.3 Male Archbold's Bowerbirds decorate their bower mat with plumes of adult male King of Saxony Birds of Paradise – a case of one bird species using the plumage of another to impress females of it's own kind, Tari Gap, Papua New Guinea (opposire top right).

6.4 Obana men of Papua New Guinea's Southern Highlands crown their headdresses with King of Saxony Bird of Paradise plumes and (as man with whistle in mouth) crests of gardener bowerbirds (see Figures 6.2 and 6.3).

that bowerbirds might possess an aesthetic sense while proof of it is lacking.

Of course we are still a long way from knowing if a male bowerbird busily rearranging his bower decorations is in fact aware, to any degree, of the potential influence his activity might have on the next female visiting his bower. What is clear, however, is that a male bowerbird certainly knows when something is out of place, just as a picture frame hanging crookedly on a wall will attract peoples' attention and cause them frustration until able to straighten it. The latter gives a sense of peace of mind, or satisfaction, which male bowerbirds perhaps experience in having their bower decorations where they want them. Of course the discovery that several bowerbird species use a 'tool' to apply paint to their avenue walls and the perception that vocal mimicry may be indicative of higher mental capacity greatly intensified interest in the bowerbirds and strengthened the widespread popular belief in their supposed superior intelligence.

The widespread fascination with bowerbirds continues unabated. They feature in the daily lives of the public in Australia and New Guinea just as the European Robin and Magpie in Europe and the American Robin and Blue Jay in America do. Indeed, bowerbirds are perceived as epitomising the Australian avifauna almost as much as are Emus and Kookaburras. As a result of their colourful and amusing behaviour bowerbirds are much admired, appreciated, respected, and even loved, by people sharing their habitats. The skilful bower building by male bowerbirds and the acquisitive manner in which they gather, steal, defend, and artistically display bower decorations, paint their structures, and mimic human and other sounds, in order to impress females, are characterful traits that people can closely relate to as most human-like.

Because much of what bowerbirds do is perceived to be reminiscent of some human behaviour a great many qualities of humanity have been attributed to them, this being termed anthropomorphism. Even some objective scientists, having worked with these birds over the course of their longer-term field studies, have come to consider them capable of artistic expression and the cultural transmission of this most rare of animal qualities. Who is to say that they are wrong? But then again, a consideration of digger wasps that pick up a stone in their mouths to use as a tool to stamp down sand that conceals and protects their nest entrance hole perhaps helps put the question of animal intelligence into some perspective. For few people would see this as mainstream tool use or would attribute the wasp with any mental appreciation of the future function of its efforts.

Bowerbirds in traditional cultures

Bowerbird species with more colourful adult male plumages were inevitably included in the general bird plume trade out of New Guinea. This involved skins of the Masked and Flame Bowerbirds but also, in a limited way, crested adult males of some gardener bowerbirds; Figures I.2 and 6.4.

The use of crests of adult male Streaked Bowerbirds as body decoration

by Papuans was recorded on the Kokoda Trail, of World War II infamy, of Papua New Guinea, as were the crests of Macgregor's in the Kubor Mountains of Papua New Guinea and in the Weyland Mountains of Papua. During his 1928 explorations as a naturalist in eastern New Guinea, Lee Crandall of the New York Zoo met a native policeman of Iola village on the Owen Stanley Ranges. That policeman carried a lime pot and spatula, as a necessary accessory to the chewing of betel nut. This particular spatula was made from a cassowary (a large flightless ratite bird of New Guinea and north-eastern Australia, closely related to the Emu and Ostrich) bone fitted with a rough ring at its top and this decorated by "the golden scalps of two gardener bower-birds, called *gullawalla*". They were presumably the crests of Macgregor's or Streaked Bowerbirds. The policeman was most reluctant to part with his pot and spatula, and initially insisted on removing the bowerbird crests before doing so, but eventually did trade it complete with its feather decorations. At the small village of Kekefi, near Fofofofo, Crandall reported gardener bowerbird crests also being kept, wrapped in tree bark and carefully stored in the rafters of a mens' house as part of a larger collection of mostly bird of paradise plumes. These were used as personal decoration of men during their 'sing-sings' or social dances; Figure 6.4. Such crests must have been traded down from the higher altitude habitats of gardener bowerbirds. Crests of adult male gardener bowerbirds represented virtually the only feather decoration worn by people of the Weyland Mountains; and the Dani People of the Ilaga Valley, Papua, commonly used them as ornaments prior to 1964.

Some people of Australia did, and may still, wear the dried colourful crests of adult male grey bowerbird skins as personal body adornment: Aboriginal men from the Laura area of southern Cape York Peninsula certainly wore the lilac crest of adult male Great Bowerbird to impress their women folk.

Papuan men admire male bowerbirds for their skill and artistry in accumulating and displaying what they perceive as the birds' equivalent of the bride-price or wealth that they themselves must acquire to pay the relatives of their intended wives. Today, as they undoubtedly have done for centuries, Papuan boys and men occasionally and respectfully visit the bowers of the highland moss forest-dwelling Archbold's Bowerbird. This they do in the hope of finding there the greatly treasured head plumes of the King of Saxony Bird of Paradise, which are worn by them as head dress decoration during the more important of their 'sing-sings'. Only adult male birds wear such feathers, taking seven years to mature and thus gain these plumes of adulthood for the first time; Figure 6.2. They subsequently produce only two such plumes each year with their annual moult. We made the novel discovery that male Archbold's Bowerbirds collect these extremely rare feathers in order to impress females, the very reason Papuan men wear them, that visit their bowers. The male birds vigorously steal them from each other's bowers. Thus the male bowerbirds, Figure 6.3, just as the Papuan men, Figure 6.4, are using valued rare objects that are external to their bodies to, in part, *symbolize* their suitability as a potential mate to females of their own kind.

The bower decorating activities of male Great and, to lesser extent, Spotted Bowerbirds on the Australian landscape have recently attracted the attention of a thoughtful team consisting of one biologist and several archaeologists. They observed that the birds accumulate bower decorations that may include moderately large collections of Aboriginal, and other human, artefacts. While these will reflect certain weight, size, and colour restrictions or preferences of the birds, a significant number, given that more than 1000 stone pieces have been counted in a single bower, of artefacts may be accumulated at more traditional bower sites. In the case of an abandoned or disused traditional bower site the bower sticks would in time decompose and blow away, leaving an accumulation of human artefacts and mammal bones suggestive of human activity there; Figure 6.5. Moreover, floodwater may then disperse these discrete accumulations, over considerable distances if on a watercourse, so confusing the picture for archaeologists. Similarly a bowerbird repeatedly taking material from a human midden site to his bower might leave a misleading story behind.

Another bird clearly perceived as a thief is the Tooth-billed Bowerbird:

6.5 An adult male Great Bowerbird surveys his stone and bone decorations from within his bower avenue, Charters Towers, Queensland.

Norwegian explorer and collector Carl Lumholtz, Figure 6.6, noting in his dramatically titled book *Among Cannibals* that it is named *gramma* by the Aboriginal people of the upland rainforests of the Australian Wet Tropics "because it steals the leaves which it uses to play with." This latter observation presumably alludes to the fact that the Aboriginal people knew full well that rival male Tooth-billed Bowerbirds steal leaves from each other's courts.

Myths about bowerbirds

Historically, Papuan and Australian indigenous people hold male bowerbirds and their works in the highest regard, respecting them for their human-like industry and artistic abilities. As a result, there are doubtless many more traditional myths about the birds and their behaviour than are presently recorded. Sadly, many of them will not be documented before lost to the collective memories of many tribal groups.

In the case of Macgregor's Bowerbird, as but one example, Papuan men may use the way a male bird removes a leaf they placed upon his bower as indicating the direction in which they should seek a wife-to-be. Papuan naturalist Saem Majnep, Figure 5.3, likens the decorating of the stick maypole bower by male Macgregor's Bowerbirds to "a man heaping up sticks of sugar cane and hanging bunches of bananas from this, to display and give away after a dance." This men of wealth do to demostrate their status as a "big man" in society. One of the most delightful of associations concerning Macgregor's Bowerbird clearly emphasises the way in which Papuans admire the males for their bower building: The Huli, or Wigmen, of the Southern Highlands of Papua New Guinea perform the taro cooking rite of *Ma*. Sticks are taken from the base of an active bower and then ceremonially used to cook taro before feeding it to a young child. In this way the highly regarded industriousness of the bowerbird is passed on to the infant.

According to anthropologist Christin K. Schmid the people of Nokopo, Finisterre Range, Papua New Guinea, consider the bower of Macgregor's Bowerbird "to be an equivalent of their men's (*sic*) ceremonial houses. They interpret male display behaviour at the bower as initiation of young male bowerbirds by their fathers... Bowerbirds and their ceremonial houses in the forest, the bowers, play a major role in mythical lore." Nokopo people do not see the bower as part of a bird's mating behaviour but as its ceremonial house where younger individuals are initiated. Consequently Nokopo men, and those of the Pasum People of the southern watershed of the Finisterre Range, used to actually build a bower reconstruction in their mens' house to present to boys passing the second stage of initiation, "thus demonstrating to them their close association with the forest and its creatures".

People near Rubi of western New Guinea informed a German ornithologist in 1873 that they do not kill the Masked Bowerbird for fear it will bring on thunder. A legend of the people of the southern watershed of the Owen Stanley Mountains

6.6 Norwegian Dr. Carl Lumholtz (1851-1922) collected wildlife in Queensland during 1880-1883 and is best known for his dramatically titled book *Among Cannibals*.

6.7 An Aboriginal carving of a male Great Bowerbird, in nape presentation courtship posture, by a Central Australian artist of the Northern Territory, *c.* 1995.

of Papua New Guinea relates that Fawn-breasted Bowerbirds' bowers will not burn because, when threatened by fire, the male owner wets his plumage to then damp down his bower sticks to prevent them from catching fire. Likewise at Bom village on the northern watershed of the Finisterre Mountains Tom Gilliard was told by an old man that people killed this bird by placing a saucer of water beside the bower before setting fire to the bower. The bower owner would then wet himself in the water and leap at the fire in an attempt to put it out. In this way the birds were tricked into killing, if not also cooking, themselves.

According to a legend of the native people of the Darwin area of tropical northern Australia *Weedah* the Great Bowerbird inherited the spirit of tribal chief *Weedapinya* the soothsayer of shells who had an obsession for shells that he collected and carried with him. The shells were his source of power, enabling him to lead his people to rich hunting grounds and water. Upon his death his spirit was transferred to the body of the Great Bowerbird that had always followed the people from camp to camp. Thus *Weedah* became the shell gatherer, and the tribe made him their totem and treat his 'camps', or bowers, with great respect.

The Gagudju people of Kakadu, in the Northern Territory of Australia, traditionally had the utmost respect for the Great Bowerbird. In their book *Kakadu* Stanley Breeden and Belinda Wright write of Nipper Kapirigi, an elder Badmardi man, explaining that "*Djuwe,* that bird, he keep ceremony. Special ceremony for business [anything secret in Aboriginal ceremonial life]. He dance and sing like ceremony. He build special hut to keep bones. He keep our special initiation ceremony; that's his job. But you gotta be careful. That bird dangerous, he kill you and steal your bones." Aboriginal artists include creatures of their environment in their work today that they do not necessarily include traditonally. Stanley Breeden once obtained a carving of a great bowerbird by an aboriginal artist in central

Australia as a gift for us. The result captures a male bird in the nape presentation courtship posture in a remarkably fluid and life-like way that only someone with real knowledge of the bird and great skill could do; Figure 6.7.

Bowerbirds in contemporary cultures

There are numerous stories of bowerbirds, mostly Satin, Spotted, and Great, taking items from peoples' camps, vehicles, and homes that include jewellery, keys, and even a glass eye; Figures 6.8 and 6.9. Several bowers of the Satin located near suburban areas or campsites had, most ironically, condoms placed upon them as bower decorations!

Stories that demonstrate the way in which bowerbirds insinuate themselves into the lives of people abound and we can recite but a few examples here: A broach that had been lost from a station property was found in the bower of a Spotted Bowerbird two years later. A pair of spectacles, taken from a camp, was recovered at the bower of a Great. In 1929 Alec Chisholm wrote of a horse-drover's tale that recites how on a Queensland station in 1888 a horse-driver placed his glass eye in a cup of water outside his tent before retiring, only to find it gone the next morning. He suspected a puppy belonging to a boy in the camp. Two weeks later the horse-tailer of the same crew wished to shoot a wild horse and so, lacking bullets, he sought out a bowerbird's bower in the hope of finding some lead among its decorations so that he might produce a bullet from it. He

6.8 An adult male Satin Bowerbird includes human artifacts among his bower decorations, Lamington, Queensland.

found some lead on a bower but also found his mate's glass eye!

There are a number of stories concerning the loss of keys from a motor vehicle left open and unattended. As these instances usually involved the Spotted or Great, but also the Satin, Bowerbirds the potentially stranded people fortunately realised that a bowerbird was probably to blame and searched the surrounding habitat until finding the nearest bower – and usually also their missing keys.

So eager were male Great Bowerbirds on the Leichhardt River of Queensland for bones as bower decorations that they would perch to watch the bird collector W. S. Day eating pigeons he had shot in order to retrieve bones as they were thrown to the ground. Alfred North reports a correspondent writing of Great Bowerbird bowers "I found a very bright specimen of gold embedded in glistening white quartz, and when in the opal country I used frequently to find pieces of precious opal in and around them. At a bower near a mining camp I found two tin teaspoons, portions of a steel watch-chain, a bright sixpence, eleven tin tobacco-tags, and a few horseshoe nails. The miners do not like these birds, as they pilfer any small bright articles lying about the camp to ornament their bowers; also for the depredations they commit in their gardens, especially among tomatoes." The latter is a common lament in referring to bowerbirds in the Australian literature. To the contrary, however, another observer noted, "near Croydon these birds are very tame and will freely enter the tents of the miners

6.9 An adult male Great Bowerbird includes human artifacts among his bower decorations, obtained from an infant school playground, Townsville, Queensland.

and charcoal-burners, who make great pets of them and will not allow them to be molested."

Some man-made items used as bower decorations can represent a threat to bowerbirds. Some male Satin Bowerbirds show a fondness for the blue plastic rings used to seal the plastic caps on milk bottles and these have been known to find their way around the neck of a bird and cause its death. As a result of this one milk bottling company went to the trouble of changing the colour of its caps and rings.

Bowerbird mimicry of human sounds

The sounds that bowerbirds mimic also make them highly endearing to people. It is perhaps the mimicry of grey bowerbirds that most people are familiar with, because they closely associate with some town and city suburbs and with property owners' homes on stations. Spotted Bowerbirds mimic the sounds of barking dogs, of cattle breaking through scrub vegetation, mammals walking over ground litter, emus crashing through wire fencing, wood-chopping, a stockwhip being used, and even that of the human voice. Egg collectors noted that a female Western Bowerbird mimicked the call of a young goat as her eggs were taken, and nesting female Great Bowerbirds mimicked cats meowing and dogs barking. A Great Bowerbird perching above a sleeping cat was continuously heard to mimic cat meowing until the cat left. A housewife in the Kimberley of Western Australia found it worrying to hear her children about the house when she knew full well that they were away at school. She was hearing her garden-resident Great Bowerbird mimicking the voices of her children at play. At Australia's Broome Bird Observatory a Great Bowerbird was recently heard to mimic conversing human voices.

Some New Guinea gardener, and Archbold's, bowerbirds have been heard to mimic mumbled human conversation. A hand-held Fawn-breasted Bowerbird on Cape York Peninsula, caught at its bower beside a ranger's residence, mimicked a person saying "Hello, good morning … (unintelligible person's name)". After three weeks filming activity at the bower of a Vogelkop Bowerbird in the Arfak Mountains a male bird was heard to imitate the noise of the squeaking legs of the cameraman's tripod. It is sadly true today that the males of some bowerbird species are increasingly likely to be heard mimicking the sound of chainsaws and trees falling; see *Bowerbird Conservation* below.

Bowerbirds as subjects of modern interest

There are numbers of popular books, films, feature articles, and company products featuring facts about and images of bowerbirds. Several species feature commonly in the public and commercial sectors of everyday contemporary life, including on postage stamps.

One of the first popular books was written in 1921: This is the undated small children's book *Spotty, the Bower Bird* by Edward S. Sorenson, a professional

6.10 Alexander H. Chisholm OBE (1890-1977) studied and photographed bowerbirds. Copyright and courtesy of the Royal Australasian Ornithologists Union.

6.11 Pioneer Australian bowerbird student and photographer Norman Chaffer AOM. (1899-1992). Copyright and courtesy of the Royal Australasian Ornithologists Union.

6.12 Professor John Warham of the University of Canterbury, New Zealand, master bird photographer and early bowerbird student. By Lance Tickell, courtesy of John Warham.

6.13 Two fine photographs of a Black-eared Catbird leaving its nest, north Queensland in 1958. By and courtesy of John Warham.

6.14 A fledgling Tooth-billed Bowerbird, north Queensland January 1959. By and courtesy of John Warham.

journalist, which appeared in Melbourne. Only 17 pages are dedicated to 'Spotty', these recounting the life story of a male Spotted Bowerbird from hatching to his death a decade later. It is written with a sound biological knowledge of the bird for the time.

An Australian pioneer student and photographer of bowerbirds was prolific natural history author Alec H. Chisholm; Figure 6.10. He published occasional articles on Australian bowerbird species from 1927 to 1966, including one with Norman Chaffer on the Golden Bowerbird. He was the first to photograph that bird at the nest. Colour photographs of bowerbirds and many illustrated feature articles about them have appeared in innumerable magazines worldwide, including National Geographic Magazine of Washington, D.C.: One of the earliest was by pioneer Australian ornithologist and bird photographer Norman Chaffer in 1961, Figure 6.11, and featured several Australian species. In 1984, when 85 years old, Chaffer published his book *In Quest of Bower Birds* about his travels in search of, and photographic experiences with, all Australian species except the Western Bowerbird.

John Warham, Figure 6.12, and his wife Pat travelled around Australia and studied and photographed, among other things, bowerbirds during 1956 and 1958-1959. These travels resulted in two of the early significant writings on wild bowerbird behaviour and some wonderful pioneering photographs of them; Figures 6.13 and 6.14. Warham went on to become Reader in Zoology at the University of Canterbury, Christchurch, New Zealand and a leading world authority on seabirds.

Because of the unique and complex behaviour that they exhibit in such animated and amusing ways, bowerbirds have featured in many television documentaries. These have including several of Sir David Attenborough's natural history series, one dealing primarily with the birds of paradise called *Attenborough in Paradise* released in 1996 and another dedicated to them called *Bowerbirds: The Art of Seduction* released in 2000. In addition, the Television New Zealand Natural History Film Unit released *Sex and Greed - the Bowerbirds* in 1991. Having been actively involved in the study of living wild bowerbirds over the past three decades the present authors were invited to act as scientific advisors to these films and to accompany the film crews into the wilds of tropical Australia and New Guinea; Figure 6.15.

Bowerbirds in art

Artist Ellis Rowan (1848-1922; Figure 6.16), termed 'Australia's Brilliant Daughter' by her biographer, made trips into the wilds of New Guinea and Australia to become an internationally acclaimed botanical artist. In addition to painting plants and insects she also painted many birds of paradise and several bowerbirds, including the Masked (twice), the Regent, and what appears to be the Western. That she was no bird illustrator is evidenced by the fact that she copied postures and the setting of birds in her Western Bowerbird painting from the plate of the Great Bowerbird in Sharpe's monographic book; see Chapter 5.

6.15 The authors and Sir David Attenborough beneath a, highly elevated, Golden Bowerbird's bower during the making of the BBC film *Bowerbirds: The Art of Seduction.* By Mike Potts.

6.16 Australian botanical artist Ellis Rowan (1848-1922) also painted birds, including several bowerbirds. Kind permission and courtesy of the National Library of Australia, Canberra.

Famous modern Australian artist Brett Whiteley (1939-1992) produced a number of works depicting birds, particularly in the 1980s and, given their prominence in Australian culture, it was perhaps inevitable that one of these was of a bowerbird. The 152 x 137 centimetre canvas shows an adult male Satin Bowerbird standing within his, highly stylised, avenue bower with a blue decoration held in his bill and others on the ground in front of the bower. The bower stands in the middle of an unrelieved expanse of desert sand, the moon just visible above the flat horizon, above which is a clear blue sky dotted with stars. While the arid habitat is clearly ecologically inappropriate, Whiteley has produced a most striking and iconic Australian image by incorporating it into his painting.

American artist Mary Jo McConnell, Figure 6.17, is presently engaged

6.17 American artist Mary Jo McConnell in her studio with her paintings of Vogelkop Bowerbirds' bowers. Kind permission and courtesy of Mary Jo McConnell.

in a long-term study of several bower-owning male Vogelkop Bowerbirds that involves the close observation of them, as developing avian artists, over nearly a decade. By revisiting the bowers of four adjacent males deep in the Arfak Mountains over more than eight years she has been able to record, in her own art works on canvas, differences in bower architecture and decoration from year to year, both within and between individuals. Her artworks and her mental and physical endurance in persuing inspiration for them are singularly impressive and highly original.

Bowerbirds as commercial symbols

Perhaps the first commercial use of bowerbirds following the plume trade was that adult plumaged males, notably of the Regent and Satin species, were once eagerly hunted for mounting as decorative household novelties, and were commonly found in cabinets of mixed stuffed birds. These can still be found now and then on the antique marketplace today.

An Australian with a tendency to hoard less-than-useful things is often fondly referred to as being a 'bit of a bowerbird'. With this commonplace descriptive phrase in mind secondhand goods retail businesses have been named 'Bowerbird Secondhand', 'Bowerbird Antiques' and the like. A trader in Cairns, north Queensland recently established his business as 'BowerShed Secondhand'; Figure 6.18.

Various contemporary Australian products feature or depict a bowerbird. For example, we found a delightful ceramic tile featuring an adult male Regent Bowerbird at his bower, in a Kangaroo Island souvenir shop way out of the range of that bird; Figure 6.19. Following the success of modern bird carvings produced in South Africa of species found there Australian Charles Smith of

Dinkum Birds of Australia included an adult male Regent Bowerbird in a range of collectable Australian species he produces; Figure 6.20. Possibly the largest image of a bowerbird ever exhibited was a highly stylised fabricated one of a flying adult male Regent. This adorned the outside wall of several upper stories of the then Mercantile Mutual Insurance (Australia) Company Ltd. building in Sydney, Australia. This image was also used as the company logo on many products, including stationery.

In 1956 the large winery and distillery Mildara Wines Ltd. of Merbein, Victoria, Australia, released *Golden Bower* Riesling as Bin 3 and continued to do so each year until Bin 25, in 1977, when the wine was discontinued. The name was one of a series of wines given a bird name and originated by H.R. Haselgrove. The illustration for the *Golden Bower* label was drawn by Wyatt Morro from ornithological books he studied in the Adelaide Museum in 1955. It is quite clearly little more than a direct copy of the upper part of the plate of the species appearing in Robert Bowdler Sharpe's monograph set into a rosette of grape vine leaves; Figure 6.21.

Given the level of interest in them in New Guinea and Australia it is not surprising to find that a few bowerbird species have featured on postage stamps of those countries. For example: an adult male and female Streaked Bowerbird,

6.18 Detail of a brick wall of a business alluding to bowerbird behaviour and depicting male Satin Bowerbirds at a bower, Cairns, Queensland. By kind permission of Martin Grossetti.

6.19 A commercial Australian ceramic tile featuring an adult male Regent Bowerbird in a bower.

6.20 A contemporary commercial 'collectable' wood carving of an adult male Regent Bowerbird. With kind permission of Charles Smith of Dinkum Birds of Australia.

6.21 The bottle label of Mildara Wines' 1956 to 1977 'Golden Bower' Riesling. Permission and courtesy of R.F. Haselgrove, Mildara Wines Ltd (left above).

6.22 A Green Catbird and a Regent Bowerbird depicted on two of a set of eight Australian bird stamps issued in 1980. Kind permission of Australian Postal Corporation, original work being held in the National Philatelic Collection (left below).

6.23 Logo of O'Reilley's Rainforest Retreat, a fine bowerbird spotting venue near Brisbane, featuring a flying adult male Regent Bowerbird based upon a Len Robinson photograph. Permission and courtesy of the O'Reilly family (below).

under the name Striped Gardener Bowerbird, adorned the one penny stamp, and a pair of Adelbert Bowerbirds the three penny stamp, of a set of 11 Territory of Papua and New Guinea (now Papua New Guinea) bird stamps issued in 1964; others in the series all being of birds of paradise. A Green Catbird, under the name Spotted Catbird, appeared as the 18 cent stamp, and an adult male Regent Bowerbird as the 35 cent stamp, of a set of eight Australian bird stamps issued in 1980; Figure 6.22. Indonesia recently released postage stamps depicting a Masked, a Lauterbach's and a Yellow-fronted Bowerbird.

Another corporate use of the Regent Bowerbird is a lifelike image of an adult male Regent in flight. This image, Figure 6.23, is based upon a photograph taken in the mid 1970s by Australian bird photographer Len Robinson. A large print of this picture long decorated the wall of the dining room of the internationally famous O'Reilly's Rainforest Retreat (formerly Guesthouse), just south of Brisbane, Queensland, and a slightly stylised logo based upon it in 1980 now adorns numerous O'Reilly's souvenirs. O'Reilly's provides one of the greatest of living bowerbird spectacles: Every day large numbers of Regents and Satins, and the odd Green Catbird, are fed by the O'Reilly family, their staff, and visitors. At such times some two-dozen adult males of both bower building species might be seen together with numerous female-plumage individuals. So much a part of the daily routine of the business have the wild bowerbirds become that large inverted bay windows have been constructed to project into the dining rooms, so that visitors might watch a hoard of feeding wild bowerbirds as they eat their own meal during daylight.

6.24 Sheikh Saoud Bin Mohammed Bin Ali Al Thani of Qatar (right) and Danish aviculturalist Simon B. Jensen, were the first to keep and breed Flame Bowerbirds. By and courtesy of Simon B. Jensen and Al Wabra Wildlife Preservation.

Bowerbirds in aviculture

Ever since the discovery of the first bower the complex behaviour of bowerbirds in building and decorating them has stimulated an interest not only in the birds in the wild but also in their maintenance and study in captivity, and in their conservation. Live bowerbirds have long been actively sought for exhibit in public aviaries, such as those within state and national zoological gardens, in part because the bower building behaviour of males adds significant entertainment and interest value not provided by other birds. Thus, live Satins were to be viewed at London's Regent Park Zoo within but a few years of their bower building habits being first made known to the western world, by John Gould in 1840. Of the 20 bowerbird species that we detail in this book we believe that at least seven or eight have been bred at least once in aviaries.

6.25 The first published image of a Flame Bowerbird's egg, laid in captivity in Qatar. By and courtesy of Simon B. Jensen and Al Wabra Wildlife Preservation.

Several bowerbird species were regularly maintained at the Baiyer River Sanctuary, in the Western Highlands of Papua New Guinea, including at various times during the 1950s to 1980s individuals of White-eared and Black-eared Catbirds, Macgregor's, Streaked, Lauterbach's and Fawn-breasted Bowerbirds. The authors studied and photographed captives there as well as birds at Lauterbach's bowers in the bush about the sanctuary. All three catbirds, the Flame, Regent, Satin, and two or three of the grey bowerbird species have been repeatedly bred in captivity in Australia and elsewhere. We suspect that at least six or seven species have never been seriously maintained in aviculture, if at all, and we are not aware of Tooth-billed or Golden Bowerbirds having ever been kept, let alone bred, in captivity.

6.26 A recently fledged Flame Bowerbird, bred in captivity in Qatar. By and courtesy of Simon B. Jensen and Al Wabra Wildlife Preservation.

British aviculturalist Marian Johnstone wrote of breeding the Satin Bowerbird in the United Kingdom as long ago as 1902. Arnold Hirst bred Satin Bowerbirds in captivity in Sydney in December 1937 and maintained a resultant male offspring until it gained its first blue-black feathers at three and a half years old. This male completed attainment of its adult plumage some seven months latter but this, it must be noted, was in the absence of any rival males. In 1941 Satin Bowerbirds were bred in a large aviary enclosure, also containing Lyrebirds, at the then Sir Colin MacKenzie Sanctuary, Badger Creek, near Melbourne, under the Directorship of Australian zoologist David Fleay.

6.27 A juvenile Flame Bowerbird, bred in captivity in Qatar. By and courtesy of Simon B. Jensen and Al Wabra Wildlife Preservation.

Outstanding among keepers of bowerbirds are four men, one English, one Danish and two Australian, who not only bred them in aviaries but also, just as importantly, published useful accounts of their successes. Reginald Phillipps bred Regents in England in 1905 and 1911. Indicative of how important better avicultural practice can be to the science of ornithology is the fact that it is mostly the observations of captive breeding Regents by Phillipps that furnishes what we know of its breeding biology today. The Australian aviculturalists, who emulated the work of Phillipps, were R.E.B. Brown of Newcastle, New South Wales, who bred Regents in 1955, and Stan Sindel of Sydney who also bred them in 1987.

Danish master aviculturalist Simon B. Jensen performed a highly significant and admirable avicultural 'first' in June-July 2003 at the Al Wabra Wildlife Preservation facility of Sheikh Saoud Bin Mohammed Bin Ali Al Thani in Qatar, Middle East; Figure 6.24. He not only maintained the Flame Bowerbird in captivity for the first time but also successfully bred it in June-July 2003 and repeated the achievement during May-June of 2004; Figures 6.25 to 6.27. In so doing he learnt much about the behaviour and biology of the species and thus demonstrated the great value of genuine aviculture, the reproduction of birds in captivity as opposed to the mere keeping of them.

In 1986 Professor Jared Diamond wrote that bowerbirds "in zoos have scarcely received serious study, although observations of birds reared in captivity could be decisive for separating the contributions to bower style of inheritance and of learning." Certainly there is a great future for aviculture to significantly advance both public and scientific awareness, appreciation, and understanding of the bowerbirds. We use the word aviculture most advisedly because, their undeniable educational value in captivity notwithstanding, we believe no birds should be held captive without the opportunity to reproduce. Aside from providing the potential to learn much basic biological information for a number of little-known species, simple experimental work could throw light upon various other aspects. For example, how many years does it take the males of each species to acquire adult plumage under various circumstances? At what age are males and females able to reproduce? Is recognition of the opposite sex innate or must it be learnt? Can males build bowers in the total absence of other males during their lifetime? And there are many more such questions.

Bowerbird conservation

Collecting and shooting has rarely represented a threat to bowerbirds, although it did play a part in the decline of the Spotted in some areas. Some orchardists, market gardeners, grape growers, and owners of kitchen gardens doubtless still illegally kill some bowerbirds because they show a liking for soft fruits and green vegetables. While this may involve Regent, Satin, Spotted, Western and Great Bowerbirds in some parts of their ranges, it does not represent a serious threat to larger populations except perhaps at the most localized level; although it certainly did in the not-too-distant past with respect to Spotted in South Australia and Victoria. Great Bowerbirds are recorded as taking eggs from domestic fowls, one bird even being said to have attempted to carry an egg off in its claws! The Spotted is presently considered extinct in the state of South Australia and possibly also in Victoria, although their presence there in historical times was already geographically restricted.

Are any bowerbird species presently threatened with extinction, or even under threat of significant population decline? We do not think so. While several of the Australian species have lost parts of their previously held ranges to habitat destruction and degradation, the Green Catbird, Regent, Golden, and Spotted Bowerbirds fairly substantially so, none is rare or endangered as a species today.

Fortunately, most populations of bowerbirds appear to be stable. Indeed one or two species have in recent years moved into the suburbs of Australian cities and taken up residence there, including. Townsville, Sydney, and Canberra, because the available of water, cultivated fruiting plants and insects associated with them are beneficial to the birds. Synthetic artifacts are available where humans dwell and these are also taken advantage of by adaptable male bowerbirds.

A problem not to be underestimated is the potential impact of native and exotic predators upon the more vulnerable, court or bower attending, species. The all-too-well established feral cat populations in Australia certainly kill bowerbirds at water troughs and bores as well as at bowers. The recent and rapid extensive spread of this introduced predator through the wilds of New Guinea has the potential for real disaster for bowerbirds, especially those with restricted upland distributions. Should large-scale logging be inflicted upon some bowerbird habitats in New Guinea things could change rapidly with respect to their status. But as with the vast majority of birds, it is habitat loss and degradation through the pressure of human populations that now most seriously threatens bowerbirds; and human beings.

The ongoing status of bowerbirds requires greater vigilance in Papua and Papua New Guinea than in Australia. This should be seen as an international obligation, if warning signs of decline and increasingly precarious status are to be perceived and acted upon. Conserving bowerbirds today primarily involves ensuring that no significant further loss of habitats occurs, especially in the case of those geographically limited species. Obviously those species with most restricted ranges or habitat that are not effectively protected, notably the Yellow-fronted and Adelbert Bowerbirds of New Guinea, need to have their status and vulnerability regularly and closely assessed into the future. The relatively rare Archbold's Bowerbird is classified as 'lower risk/near threatened' by BirdLife International's review of the world's threatened birds in 2000. Much habitat suitable for this species remains intact, however, and it cannot be considered presently under threat – unless intensive logging of its habitat should be undertaken. Global warming must be viewed as an issue that has the potential to change things soon, especially with respect to limited highland species.

There remains much to examine, test and learn with respect to the origins and functions of bowerbird mating systems, bowers, ecology, and behaviour and their meaningful conservation requires such knowledge. While a team of most eminent biologists wrote of the bowerbirds, in the 1987 book *Save the birds*, "… that any of them should become extinct through human neglect is surely unthinkable." this is, alas, not impossible in this age of widespread and wholesale habitat destruction. What is presently known about all of the 20 bowerbird species is comprehensively summarised in Chapter 7.

PART III

THE BOWERBIRD FAMILY

A parent Black-eared Catbird feeds its nestling a fruit,
Paluma Range, north Queensland.

7

The bowerbird species

WHITE-EARED CATBIRD

Ailuroedus buccoides

Etymology: *s Ailuroedus* Gr. *ailouros*, a cat; *odos*, a singer. *buccoides* Mod. L. *bucco*, barbet; Gr. *-oides*, resembling a barbet (a bird of the family Captionidae).

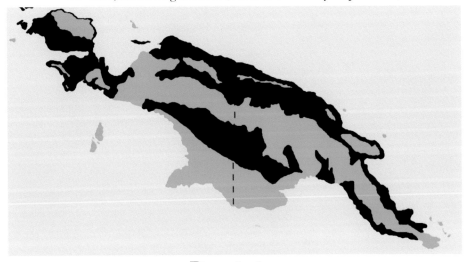

Found throughout New Guinea lowlands, including Salawati, Batanta, Waigeo and Yapen Islands, up to 800 metres above sea level but locally occurs higher (to 1200 m). This catbird is typically replaced by the Black-eared Catbird at higher elevations, but shares habitat with the latter in some hill forest including on the Sogeri Plateau. In southeast New Guinea this appears to be the lowland catbird and the Black-eared the montane one, whereas in the lowlands of southern New Guinea both catbirds occur but with mutually exclusive distributions.

Description

A large and compact, inconspicuously shy but vocal, songbird of New Guinea. Differs from the Black-eared Catbird in its unmarked dark brown to tan crown, distinctive white ear patch, and conspicuous black ventral spotting. The species includes four geographical forms, or subspecies; see page 291.

24 to 25 cm in length: A stout small catbird with a crown colour variable from mid brown to an almost blackish olive-brown, washed greenish. Wings and tail rich parrot green with white spots on some flight feather tips. Underparts a variable buff heavily spotted with black and the face white with black streaking and spotting except for an obvious and clear white ear patch. Bill almost whitish, eye deep red; legs pale greyish washed olive. The sexes are alike; females average smaller than males. For pictures of this bowerbird elsewhere see page 109.

Ecology and habits

Predominantly inhabits lowland and hill, but also monsoon, forest in the southeast. Found singly, in pairs, or in family parties typically of three individuals and usually wary and retiring, but inquisitive. Individuals often remain at a spot for a while, but also bound quickly along logs, branches, and the ground by long hops, and visit forest floor pools to drink and bathe. Birds call from dense vegetation: Territorial song includes an unpleasant prolonged harsh churring, almost a grating, sound. Also given are a low hissing or rasping,

Illustration of White-eared Catbirds from Sharpe's *Monograph of the Paradiseidae and Ptilonorhynchidae* of 1891-1898 (opposite).

An adult White-eared Catbird, Karawari River, Papua New Guinea.

and a cat-like nasal *meeyaaah*. Pairs maintain contact with brief high-pitched metallic sharp *tink* or *chink* notes.

Fruits and animals, mostly insects, are eaten with both being taken from foliage of the forest substage to midstage and, rarely, the canopy. As these catbirds often take adults of small birds from nets set by ornithologists they doubtless also eat nestlings of other bird species. They occasionally feed among aggregations of other fruit eating birds, and probably frequent the forest floor more than is appreciated.

Courtship and breeding

Courting pairs perform silent vigorous chases though low foliage and on the ground. They form a social bond to breed together monogamously for one or more seasons within a territory they defend from others of their kind. That numbers of adults visit water holes at other times suggests that they are less territorial out of the breeding season.

Breeding occurs in most months of the year across the species range, and may occur twice in a year at some localities as recorded at Crater Mountain, Papua New Guinea. The few records of eggs in nests are for January, April to June, and November; for nestlings May-June; and for females in breeding condition February to May, August, September, and December. A pair near Port Moresby had a several week old juvenile in attendance in mid June.

Nests are about two to three metres above ground and built among the bases of pandanus tree fronds or in a branch fork near the top of a slender leafy sapling. The nest is a sturdy bowl of stout forked twigs and a few large leaves, lined with many short sections of strong, slender, stems with a shallow eggcup depression. Eggs are plain creamy-buff; nine single egg clutches average 41 x

28 millimetres. Only single egg wild clutches are known, but up to three egg clutches were laid in captivity. In captivity the incubation periods of 21 clutches ranged from 17 or 18 to 24 days and nestling periods of 16 young from 17 to 23 days, nestlings being 18 to 24 days old at leaving the nest. Nestlings are fed fruits and animals. One wild juvenile remained with its parents for more than three and a half months after it left its nest.

Status and conservation

While easily considered scarce if not heard calling, this catbird appears to be common and widespread throughout most of its range, but uncommon in the Ok Tedi area of Papua New Guinea.

An adult White-eared Catbird, near Baiyer River, Papua New Guinea.

BLACK-EARED CATBIRD

Ailuroedus melanotis
Etymology: *Ailuroedus* Gr. *ailouros*, a cat; *odos*, a singer. *melanotis* Gr. *melas*,
black; *otis*, eared.

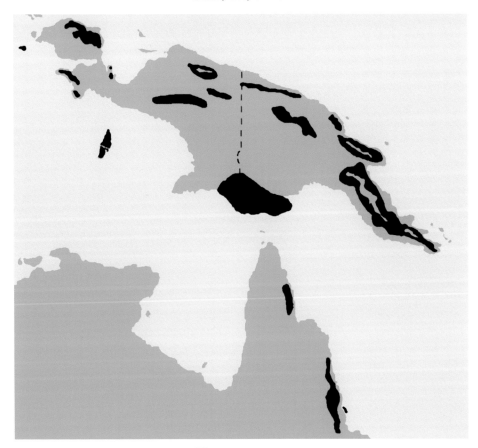

Widespread in New Guinea hill and lower montane forest at 600-1700, exceptionally 2250, metres above sea level, including Misool Island, and thus at higher altitudes than White-eared Catbirds. Locally present in south Trans-Fly River lowlands of Papua New Guinea. The usual altitudinal transition between this and the White-eared Catbird is at about 800 to 900 metres. Also occurs in tropical northeastern Queensland, Australia, from Cape York southward to Paluma Range and Mount Halifax at 0-1540, but mostly 600-900, metres in the uplands of the Wet Tropics. There is possibly some dispersal to lower altitudes in winter, at least in Australia.

Description

A large, compact, powerful, long-legged, retiring but vocally conspicuous, green songbird with contrasting black and white facial markings and a spotted crown. The species includes 10 geographical forms, or subspecies, eight in New Guinea and two in northeastern Australia; see page 291.

28 to 29 cm in length: A stout medium-sized catbird with a black crown spotted white to buff. Wings and tail rich parrot green with white spots on some flight feather tips. Underparts variably green to buffy-green heavily and broadly streaked whitish. Facial areas are of contrasting black and finely marked white feathering, but with a conspicuous black ear patch. Bill almost whitish, eye deep red; legs variably pale. The sexes are alike; females average smaller than males. New Guinea birds are larger than Australian ones. For pictures of this bowerbird elsewhere see pages 34, 56, 57, 94, 97, 106, 132, 149, 160-161.

Ecology and habits

A secretive bird that is far more often heard than seen. It is encountered singly,

Illustration of Black-eared Catbirds from Sharpe's *Monograph of the Paradiseidae and Ptilonorhynchidae* of 1891-1898 (opposite).

in pairs, or as family groups. Birds occur in lowland and upland rainforest and adjacent tall secondary growth, wet sclerophyll forest (more so in winter), and in monsoon woodland and scrub of the south Trans-Fly only. In southeast Papua birds inhabit heavy mixed, particularly riverine, rainforest to open *Eucalyptus-Melaleuca* forests.

A local dialect of this bird's loud cat-like wailing song is heard through the year across the species' range. Pairs maintain contact by sharp high-pitched single or double *tick* or *tic* notes. Infrequent *sneeze*-like sounds as well as harsh and typically bowerbird scold notes are given, but not vocal mimicry. Calling levels decline during non-breeding months, with peak calling during early morning and late afternoon.

Some adults live for more than 20 years. Predators of them include Lesser Sooty Owls and Grey Goshawks. Upon seeing a potential predator adults often adopt a motionless upright posture with tightly sleeked plumage. When strong direct sunlight strikes them birds might adopt a sunning posture, with erect breast, rump, head, and nape feathers, down-pressed tail, and drooped wings.

This catbird eats fruits and animals, mostly insects, but predominantly the former. It feeds upon a wide variety of plants' fruits, as well as some flowers, flower buds, leaves, stems, and tree sap. Because fruits are most of the diet foraging is mainly in the forest canopy, but birds do occasionally feed in the subcanopy, understorey, or on the ground where they take fruits and animals from leaf litter.

Little is known about the diet in New Guinea but fruits, especially figs, form the majority of it. Birds sometimes eat fruits placed as decorations upon the bowers of Flame and Adelbert Bowerbirds. Much more is known about the diet of Australian birds, based on our long-term study on the Paluma Range, north Queensland, where about 90% of the diet is fruit. Some 80% of fruit eating involves drupes and berries, but some capsular fruits are eaten. Fruits are mostly

An adult Black-eared Catbird, Paluma Range, north Queensland.

An adult Black-eared Catbird, Atherton Tableland, north Queensland.

searched for and then plucked while perching upright, a bird often leaning out to pull a fruit off the plant to swallow it whole. Birds also infrequently sally to snatch a fruit in flight. Larger fruits, such as figs, are torn and eaten in bits *in situ* or carried to a nearby tree bough to be eaten. Flowers, flower buds and stems, and sap are eaten *in situ*. Animal foods include worms, cockroaches, termites, cicadas, beetles, caterpillars, and spiders. Prey, including termites and cicadas, are snatched in flight, gleaned from leaves, branches, and tree trunks (termites, caterpillars, spiders) or foraged from leaf litter (worms and other litter-dwelling invertebrates). Eggs and nestlings are taken from other birds' nests to eat or to feed to their young, and small birds caught in nets are decapitated.

Fruits may be cached atop epiphytic basket ferns, tree trunk crevices, between tree forks, or among leaf litter to be returned to for eating. Birds feed alone, or in pairs but occasionally three or four forage in a larger fruiting tree canopy together with Tooth-billed, Golden, or Satin Bowerbirds and other fruit-eating birds. Black-eared Catbirds will displace Tooth-billed and Satin Bowerbirds from ripe fruit but will be displaced themselves by larger fruit eaters such as Wompoo Fruit-Doves. Birds will visit bird feeders, but remain wary.

Courtship and breeding

Courtship involves little more than a pair hopping excitedly about tree perches and the male sometimes giving sharp *tic* notes, usually with food held in his bill, until the female remains still. The food may be passed to her after mating. The sexes form perennial socially monogamous pairs, within an all-purpose territory. Only females nest built, incubate, and brood nestlings; males feed their mate and nestlings. Males and females form long standing bonds, these being reinforced early in each season as breeding territory is re-established and defended. Pairs

An adult Black-eared Catbird, Atherton Tableland, north Queensland.

typically persist within their home range for several years, although occasionally one of the sexes forms a new partnership. In our 50 hectare Paluma study area a breeding home range averaged some 1.6 hectares, with catbirds flying an average of about 70 metres from their nest to forage, there being little overlap in the foraging ranges of adjacent nesting pairs. The dispersion of consecutive nests of a pair is typically clumped, reflecting not only a preference for particular topography but also the traditional use of a particular nest site over seasons.

Little is known about when breeding occurs in New Guinea. Eggs found from August to December, a nestling in January, and females with enlarged ovaries during March and April. Two New Guinea nests were placed about two to three metres high among forking branches of a slender rainforest substage tree. In Australia breeding starts as early as August and ends in March, but this varies with location, altitude, and seasonal weather, and nesting lasts four months on average, with the peak of egg laying being October to December. Australian nest sites are mostly on slopes falling to creeks and gullies with numerous tree ferns, lawyer palms, and epiphytic ferns, or on flatter areas with a dense understorey. We found that on the Paluma Range more than 90% of nests are built in saplings and/or climbing vines, mostly lawyer palm, at about one to seven and averaging three metres above ground, but occasionally as high as 14 metres. Nests are also built at the centre of a tree fern crown, atop an epiphytic fern, or within the anastomosing roots of strangler figs.

Nests are large, bulky, deep, open, bowls consisting of a sparse to substantial foundation of large sticks forming a supportive platform beneath and around the lower nest cup. The deep nest cup consists mainly of large green to dried leaves, a layer, sometimes substantial, of decaying wood and/or mud pieces on top of the central leafy bowl, and an inner nest eggcup lining of fine twiglets and supple vine tendrils. Whilst most nests are laid in within two weeks of their completion, some are not laid in for four weeks after it.

Eggs are smooth, slightly glossy, and uniformly creamy-white or buff. Twenty-two New Guinea eggs average 43 x 30 millimetres, and 289 Australian eggs 41 x 29 millimetres. The New Guinea clutch consists of one (90% of 20 clutches) or two eggs. In Australia one to three eggs are laid but most clutches (83% of 172) are of two. Eggs are laid on alternate days and usually hatch in the order in which they were laid, on the same day or on consecutive days, up to 23 hours later. The incubation period is 22 to 23 days and the nestling period 19 to 20 days in Australia. Females cease brooding once nestlings are 15 days old. Overall nestling-feeding rate is greater for broods of two than for one. One adult-sized juvenile we banded as a nestling, 49 days out of its nest, was giving soft begging noises whilst following its parents, some 50 metres from the nest it had left.

The nestling diet includes fruits of dozens of plant species and families, with the fruits of figs the most important. The nestling diet on the Paluma Range was 80% fruits and the remainder animals. Large insects, beetles and cicadas, and pieces of birds represented some half of all animal foods fed to nestlings. Parts of small songbirds, decapitated heads of pigeon squabs, and earthworms are fed to nestlings. Sometimes a parent forages on the ground near the nest, to repeatedly feed young on litter-dwelling invertebrates. Larger items, such as a fig or a nestling bird, are often dismantled on the ground near to the nest and repeatedly returned to until all is fed to the brood.

Pairs will re-nest, following the loss of a clutch or brood early in a season, but there is no evidence of two broods being raised in a single season. The overall success rate for 63 nests on the Paluma Range was 57%, the average number of fledged young produced per adult pair each season being one. Predators of nest contents include White-tailed Rats. In departing a nest containing eggs or small nestlings the female typically raises herself to then glide quickly down and away from the nest tree. If a nest is disturbed a parent often hops to the ground to perform a 'distraction' display involving a slow, open wing-fluttering, stumbling crawl over floor to draw the predator away from the nest.

Status and conservation

This is a common and widespread bird throughout its range. It was observed at Derongo, at 600 metres above sea level, and heard throughout mid-montane forests of the Ok Tedi area of Papua New Guinea but oddly subsequently unrecorded there during four years.

GREEN CATBIRD

Ailuroedus crassirostris
Etymology: *crassirostris* L. *crassus,* thick or heavy; *rostris,* bill or billed.

Occupies the central coastal zone of eastern Australia, from the Dawes Range area in the north to due east of about Canberra, Australian Capital Territory, at near sea level up to above 1000 metres.

Description

A large, stocky, powerful, long-legged, shy and inconspicuous but highly vocal all-green bowerbird of subtropical Australian rainforests and adjacent dense habitats.

30 to 32 cm. A large, stout, entirely green catbird, with an indistinct white 'shoulder' mark and white spots on the tips of some flight feathers, and the underparts broadly streaked whitish. A ring of white feathers encircles the deep red eyes. Bill whitish, legs variably pale. The sexes are alike; adult males average slightly larger than adult females. For pictures of this bowerbird elsewhere see pages 98, 132.

Ecology and habits

A bird primarily of subtropical rainforest, although not uncommonly seen in the associated habitats of rainforest edges, adjacent eucalypt forest and woodland, gardens and orchards. Favours watercourses, especially for nesting. Birds drink and bathe in tree crevices and forest floor pools and streams, and also bathe by clinging to wet foliage and shaking and flapping their plumage. The

Illustration of Green Catbirds from Sharpe's *Monograph of the Paradiseidae and Ptilonorhynchidae* of 1891-1898 (opposite).

vocal repertoire consists of variable cat-like wailing and sneeze-like song and sharp high-pitched tick or tic contact notes, but not mimicry. Males give a more powerful and prolonged territorial song than females. Calling declines during the non-breeding season, with peak daily calling during early morning and late afternoon. A bird banded as an adult lived at least another 13 years.

This bird eats a wide variety of fruit, that constitutes more than 70% of its diet, as well as some flowers, buds, leaves, leaf buds, shoots, succulent stems, leaf petioles of tree and vine leaves and animals, mostly insects. Birds eat a large proportion of drupe and berry fruits, and occasionally also capsular ones, and figs form a major proportion of their fruit diet. Most foraging takes place in the forest canopy, above nine metres, but also occasionally on the forest floor. Most fruits are taken by birds perching upright and plucking or by sallying and plucking. Larger fruits are eaten in situ. Like the Black-eared this catbird also caches fruits, mostly figs. Cache sites include atop a bird's nest fern, in vertical and horizontal tree forks, the hollow end of a limb, and knobs or holes on tree trunks. Individuals forage in fruiting trees with other fruit eating birds, including Satin and Regent Bowerbirds.

Animals eaten include grasshoppers, cicadas, longicorn and other beetles and their larvae, millipedes, termites, and tree frogs. Invertebrates are mostly gleaned from tree foliage, epiphytes, twigs, branches, and trunks but occasionally are sallied or hawked. Birds also descend to the ground in search of animal life. One individual was observed taking a nestling from a Rufous Fantail nest. Birds will visit bird feeders but warily.

This alert adult Green Catbird shows the lack of any black facial markings and the obvious white collar patch characteristic of its species (opposite).

Courtship and breeding

Pairs intensely chasing in and about tree canopies at appropriate times of year are thought to be courting. The sexes form perennial socially monogamous pairs within an all-purpose territory. Only females built nests, incubate, and brood nestlings. Males feed their mates throughout the year, mostly figs but during pre-egg laying also insects and their larvae; females begging as they do so. Pairs breed together for one or more seasons in a nesting territory that they defend from other catbirds. Most annual foraging is confined to a home range of a little over a hectare, and during nesting to a territory of half a hectare when parents range an average of about 38 metres from their active nest.

Annual breeding is from mid September to March but its timing varies with location, altitude, and seasonal weather and may relate to the ripening of figs. The duration of annual nesting is about four months, with October to December being peak egg laying months. Nests are mostly in forks of small to large trees, typically understorey ones with densely foliaged crowns, and vine tangles atop epiphytic ferns. They are large, bulky, open cups consisting of a foundation of sticks and twigs; a discrete deep, compact, and substantial, bowl of large dried leaves and a few vine stems within the stick foundation; a layer of decaying wood and sometimes the earthy matter of epiphytic ferns; and a finer twiglet and vine tendril eggcup lining.

Eggs are plain buff; 103 eggs average 43 x 30 millimetres. One to three eggs form the clutch but most (84% of 87 clutches) consist of two, eggs being laid on alternate days. At three nests in the Beaury State Forest, New South Wales, the incubation period was 23 to 24 days and the nestling period about 21 days. Female's brood nestlings after they are 15 days old, contrary to Black-eared Catbirds, spending an average of 10% of each day brooding nestlings of 11 to 20 days old. The overall nestling feeding rate is greater for broods of two than it is for single nestling broods. One juvenile remained partially dependant upon its parents for food for at least 72 days after it left its nest, and two others were independent some 80 days after fledging.

The nestling diet is about 70% fruit and the remainder animals; figs being an important component of the fruit diet and beetles, cicadas, millipedes, and pieces of other birds the main animal foods. Alarmed parents perform 'distraction' displays on the ground near nests containing eggs or nestlings, or near their fledglings. These displays sometimes involve a parent feigning a broken wing or leg, hopping over the ground with head low, wings and slightly fanned tail hanging down.

Pairs will re-nest following the loss of a clutch or brood, particularly if it occurs early in a season, but there is no evidence of two broods being raised within a season. The overall success of 25 nests was 65%; each nesting pair averaging one successfully fledged young per season. Predators of nestlings and adults include Grey Goshawks.

Status and conservation

Fairly common and widespread throughout its present range wherever extensive habitat remains, but rare or absent in isolated rainforest patches of 2.5 hectares or smaller. The New South Wales population has become disjunct, with breaks between Merimbula and Bateman's Bay, in the Sydney and Central Coast districts and the Hunter, Boyd, and Clarence River Valleys. Some movements do occasionally take place.

An adult Green Catbird takes a daylight rest on its roosting perch.

TOOTH-BILLED BOWERBIRD

Scenopoeetes dentirostris
Etymology: *Scenopoeetes* Gr. *skene*, a house; *poietes*, a maker. *dentirostris* L. *dens,*
dentis, a tooth; *-rostris,* billed.

Confined to the Atherton
Region, Australian Wet Tropics,
from Big Tableland in the
north to Mount Elliot, near
Townsville, in the south, at 350
to 1220, but more typically 600
to 900, metres above sea level.
During winter months of dry
years some individuals move to
lower altitudes.

Description

A medium-large, solidly compact, dark-billed, drably plumaged bowerbird
predominantly confined to upland rainforests of the Australian Wet Tropics.

27 cm in length: A stout-bodied and stout-billed bowerbird that is entirely
brown-olive above and whitish below heavily streaked with brownish-olive. An
indistinct rust coloured ring of fine feathers encircles the dark brown eyes. Bill
black, legs variably mid grey; eye dark deep brown, almost blackish. Adult male
mouth interior blackish to black, that of young males and females paler and
more orange-yellow. The sexes are alike. For pictures of this bowerbird elsewhere
see pages 35, 54, 59, 71, 94, 116, 149.

Ecology and habits

Lives mostly in upland rainforests but will occupy remnant forest patches within
pasture, provided they are not too far from extensive forest. Males are loudly
vocal at courts but birds are otherwise cryptic and inconspicuous, especially in
winter when silent, immobile, and largely leaf eating. On the Paluma Range,
north Queensland males travel on average 60 metres from their active courts

Illustration of Tooth-billed
Bowerbirds from Sharpe's
Monograph of the Paradiseidae
and Ptilonorhynchidae of 1891-
1898 (opposite).

to forage or collect leaves for court decoration directly from trees or by stealing them from neighbouring courts, but will travel at least 400 metres to creeks to drink or bathe. Birds also drink from water-filled tree cavities. We once watched two birds anting on a lawn, by wiping ants held in their beak along their wings and tail; a behaviour thought to deter feather-dwelling parasites.

Males give loud advertisement vocalisations from perches near their courts, and a quieter subsong, or whisper song, during courtship display. Court advertisement song includes single *squeal, screetch* and *chuck* notes, continuous *babble* and the mimicry of other birds' song and other sounds. They are great mimics, with the calls of more than 40 other bird species being recorded including those of Golden and Satin Bowerbirds. Sometimes males will mimic opportunistically, which is to say in immediate response to other calling birds. They also mimic fruit bats, frogs, crickets, and cicadas, and during courtship their subsong includes the mimicry of many birds, some insects, often a sound like that of a drop of water hitting the surface of a pool and is culminated with a loud *tuck-tic* 'lip-smacking' sound.

Some males live for more than 24 years: one immature male took at least four years to become the owner of a traditional site and then attended it for at least 20 years. Males roost directly above their courts at night. Predators of adult Tooth-bills include Lesser Sooty Owls and Grey Goshawks. A court-owning adult male may adopt a static and sleeked posture when a rival male or female, or other bird such as a predator, visits his court or its vicinity.

Tooth-billed Bowerbirds are primarily plant eaters, with fruit representing about 80% and leaves about 15% of their diet on the Paluma Range. They also eat flowers, leaves, and stems, supplemented with animals during the breeding season. Because fruit constitutes the vast majority of the spring and summer diet, their foraging occurs mainly in the canopy. Some 70% of fruits eaten are drupes and berries, but some capsular fruits are also taken. Fruits are mostly plucked while birds perch upright, but they will infrequently sally to snatch a fruit in flight. Larger fruits are torn and eaten in bits *in situ* or plucked and carried in the bill to a nearby tree bough to be eaten there. Birds usually forage alone but in large fruiting tree canopies, such as those of figs, many might form aggregations with other fruit eating birds including Black-eared Catbirds and Satin and Golden Bowerbirds.

Leaves and succulent stems are particularly important to the winter diet, when less fruit is available. The Tooth-bill's beak is highly adapted to this most unusual songbird diet, known as folivory. Specialized notches, cusps, or 'teeth', on their lower mandible cutting edges fit into reciprocal indentations in the upper mandible when the bill is closed, to crush and masticate. This folivory typically involves biting or tearing off pieces of leaf and then manipulating it by the mandibles to be repeatedly folded into a compact wad before masticated and ingested. Animal foods include cockroaches, termites, earwigs, beetles, caterpillars, other insect larvae, and spiders but not snails. Birds will sally for and hawk termites and cicadas.

An adult male Tooth-billed Bowerbird sings above his leaf-decorated court, Paluma Range, north Queensland (opposite).

A singing adult male Tooth-billed Bowerbird hides from a visiting female behind his court display tree, Paluma Range, north Queensland.

Courts and courtship

This bowerbird reproduces polygynously, the promiscuous males seasonally clearing and decorating terrestrial courts. Our studies in 50 hectares on the Paluma Range showed that court sites, particularly long-established traditional ones, are densely distributed, at about two per hectare at 60 metres apart, on hilltops and contiguous slopes or ridges. On less favoured topography and habitat, such as steep slopes, flatter areas dissected by creeks, disturbed forest, they are more dispersed at less than one per hectare and more than 100 metres apart. Thus, courts are not evenly dispersed throughout rainforest, but are clumped over suitable topography to form exploded leks. These are leks in which the males are not typically in visual contact, as males of a true lek are, but are in vocal contact. The average home range of four adjacent court-attending males we radio-tracked during one season was 9.5 hectares, with an average overlap of 50%.

Established courts sites are traditional and some persist for in excess of 22 years. Of 82 court sites in one area near Paluma, 48% were traditional and consistently used for a decade or more: Only one of 39 courts established for 10 or more seasons was deserted over that period. Fidelity to a single court site by individual adult males was also extremely high with 71% of our marked birds attending but one for more than 16 seasons. Moreover several older adult male showed their reluctance to relinquish a precise traditional court location, having been kept from it by tree falls, by returning to it once it again became available as the obstruction rotted away years later. One adult male attended his traditional site for at least 20 years. Immature males establish rudimentary courts near or between the long-established sites of adult males. If persistent there, in the face of competition by their older neighbours, such males may eventually take over an adjacent traditional court site.

Males re-clear traditional courts at the start of each display season, on exactly the same patch of forest floor as previously or within a few metres of it. Relocation of a court within the traditional site sometimes occurs at the start of a season, especially if a male has newly inherited it; the average distance of relocation being 12 metres. This court clearing commences during August or September, but sometimes in July if fruit is already abundant. Initially a few leaves are placed upon a traditional site with little or no leaf litter clearance but leaf placement and court clearance then increases as the season progresses to the peak activity of October to December. During months of peak activity court attendance levels are highest between 0600 and 0900 hours but still remain relatively high during the day unless it is particularly hot and dry. The onset of the wet season, during January to March, terminates court-based activity, but significant dry spells thereafter result in a brief return to poorly cleared and decorated courts during February to April. This is partly post-moult activity that is mostly performed by relatively young males, as occurs in other bowerbird species.

An adult male Tooth-billed Bowerbird exposes himself from behind his display tree in initial visual courtship display, Paluma Range, north Queensland.

An adult male Tooth-billed Bowerbird approaches a female across his court in full courtship display, Paluma Range, north Queensland.

The cleared area of better-established courts of older males varies greatly, and can be as large as four by two metres and decorated with up to 180 fresh leaves. Court areas typically encompass the base of at least one trunk of a large sapling or more substantial tree, usually located near one end of the longer court axis. The ground to at least one side of this tree trunk is clear of litter and decoration leaves. During peak display activity fresh leaves are brought to courts each day and placed upon it with their paler side uppermost to produce maximum contrast, while older ones are discarded to the court periphery. Decoration leaves vary geographically, with males of populations showing different preferences of plant species. Elsewhere a wider variety of leaf species typically decorate courts, and a particular local preference can change seasonally.

During peak display periods adult males average more than 60% of daylight at their courts. Seasonal variation in time invested at courts varies from year to year, however, subject to weather conditions, particularly excessive drought and resultant food availability. For example: during a season when food was plentiful we found that Tooth-bills spent 79% of daylight attending courts whereas during an excessively dry season, with a poor fruit crop, attendance was 52%.

Males spend more than 90% of their court time singing from favoured perches above or about their court. Their remaining time is spent maintaining the court, displaying with or without a female present, and chasing off other males intent on stealing leaves. Leaf theft is particular rife between males of adjacent courts. Having noted a neighbour is not calling a court owner will fly to the unattended court and steal leaves from it.

As one of his kind approaches a court-owning adult male rapidly drops onto his court and hides behind the base of his display tree trunk to continue singing. If the visitor is a female he changes his load advertisement song to a quiet subsong that includes sophisticated vocal mimicry. If the female reaches the court this vocal display is suddenly followed by a brief but most vigorous visual display: The male hops out from behind the tree and rushes toward her with widely open mouth, pale throat feathers erected to form a conspicuous 'beard', and repeatedly flaps his widely opened wings. If the female holds her ground in the face of this aggressive advance the male often mates upon reaching her.

Breeding

Birds breed from September to January, their egg laying peaking during November and December. Nests are typically in densely-foliage vine tangles suspended from or about a tree branch or trunk at eight to 27, and averaging 15, metres above ground. The nest is a sparse foundation of sticks, sometimes with orchid stems, and a shallow eggcup lining of finer twigs. Eggs are plain buff; 61 eggs average 42 x 29 millimetres. Of 39 clutches 82% were of two eggs and the rest of one. The incubation and nestling periods are unknown. Whole fruits and insects, particularly beetles, are fed to offspring. A female will vigorously chase other Tooth-bills from within several metres of her nest and nestlings, and one performed a distraction display by flying to the ground to dash about her recently fledged young as it was approached by a person. A parent was observed feeding a juvenile in April.

Status and conservation

A study of active courts present before and after logging over 18.4 hectares of rainforest on the Mount Windsor Tableland during September to October showed that immediately following the logging the previously constantly present 11 courts were reduced by five. As the only threat to existing populations (other than global warming) would be intensive logging, if not clear felling, of what are now fully protected rainforests the Tooth-billed Bowerbird is not under pressure.

MACGREGOR'S BOWERBIRD

Amblyornis macgregoriae
Etymology: *Amblyornis* Gr. *amblus*, dull or blunt; *ornis*, a bird. *macgregoriae*
after Lady Mary Macgregor wife of Sir William Macgregor.

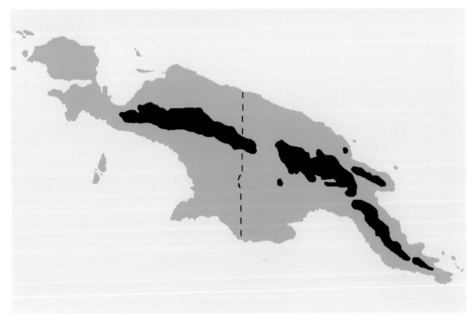

Peculiar to the mountains of east and central New Guinea at 1000 to 3000, but more typically 1600 to 2300, metres above sea level. Widespread on the central mountains west to Weyland Mountains, Papua, and also on Aldelbert Range, Huon Peninsula, Mount Bosavi, and southern Karius Range, Papua New Guinea. Replaced at lower altitude by the Streaked Bowerbird with which it overlaps infrequently and rarely hybridises with.

Description

A medium sized, compact, solid, large-crested, and inconspicuous shy montane forest bowerbird. Even males at bowers are elusive. The species includes seven geographical forms, or subspecies; see page 291.

26 cm in length: A large, plump, entirely dark brownish-olive gardener bowerbird species in which adult males differ from females and immature males in having an extensive, broad, erectile, orange crest arising from the rear crown and nape. Bill blackish, paler at its base, eye dark brown; legs dark bluish-grey. Adult males and females are similar in size. For pictures of this bowerbird elsewhere see pages 36, 72, 95, 118, 120, 121.

Ecology and habits

This bowerbird's habitat is typically primary tall mixed montane and southern *Nothofagus* beech rainforest, and rarely moss, or cloud, forest. The overall average distance that adult males travel from their bowers on Mt Missim, Papua New Guinea, is about 88 metres, although they will travel as far as 800 metres in order to steal decorations from bowers of rival males. Birds are encountered singly but sometimes as small feeding aggregations in trees with or without other fruit eating birds.

The repertoire of males' vocalisations, during both advertisement singing and courtship subsong, is diverse and includes avian and other vocal mimicry and ventriloquistic qualities. Sounds mimicked include various harsh tearing

Colour illustration of adult male Macgregor's (upper) and Yellow-fronted (lower) Bowerbirds from Sharpe's *Monograph of the Paradiseidae and Ptilonorhynchidae* of 1891-1898 (opposite).

187

sounds, growls, thuds, tappings, hollow to clear whistles, the characteristic territorial 'machine gun' call of the Brown Sicklebill bird of paradise, and human sounds, including tree felling and mumbled conversation. Flight of adult males about bowers produces a whirring that they also vocally mimic. A quieter subsong is given during courtship, involving soft whirring or *zishshing* sounds audible from only a few metres, which typically includes high-quality avian vocal mimicry.

Fruits dominate the diet but animals, mostly insects, are taken. The fruits of numerous tree, shrub, and vine species are augmented with flower parts. On Mt Missim, about 95% of fruits eaten are of the drupe and berry type, but capsular fruits are taken little. Fruit is mostly taken by the bird perching to eat it *in situ*. Several of the trees important to the diet are most common along ridges and slopes, where most bowers are located. By placing bowers on ridges, males apparently have better access to fruits and are in the best position to attract females feeding at these food plants. Bower-owning males cache fruits about their bowers.

Bowers and courtship

This bowerbird breeds polygynously, its promiscuous males seasonally decorating terrestrial bowers of the, simple, maypole type. Traditional bower sites are regularly and linearly spaced along forested ridges. Inter-bower distances on Mt Missim averaged about 180 metres; one bower was in continual use for more than 20 years. Adult males confine their activities away from bower sites to abutting home ranges. At the start of the display season adult males defend their entire home range against rivals, but once breeding begins most defence is restricted to bower sites within 150 to 200 metres about the bower. Immature and subadult males often establish rudimentary ephemeral bowers mid-way between main bower structures at established sites. Rudimentary bowers are often found at lower altitudes than the traditional ones built by older males.

Bowers of adult males are typically a roughly conical tower of sticks placed about a slender sapling(s) or tree fern trunk up to five metres tall, and built atop a thick circular, saucer-shaped, mossy mat platform raised at its circumference into an elevated rim. Their towers have a diameter at its widest point of up to 50 centimetres. The moss mat is about one metre in diameter, with the raised rim up to 75 centimetres above the inner mat. The upper dished platform is decorated with fruits, charcoal, berries, fungi and other items that include tree resin, mammal dung, lichen, flowers, leaves, beetle elytra, butterfly wings, and sometimes man-made items. Stick ends of the lower column are hung with insect frass and vegetable matter. Odd bowers may have two adjacent towers of sticks. Rudimentary bowers mostly consist of a clearing around a sapling base with or without a small accumulation of sticks. Bowers on the Huon Peninsula are different to those elsewhere, being constructed on the side of a ridge with

A typical Macgregor's Bowerbird maypole bower, Tari Valley Slopes, Papua New Guinea.

their decorated side facing down slope. These have a far broader lower section to their stick tower, which partly covers the bower mat, the base of which is decorated with tree fern-like fibres rather than moss.

On Mount Missim adult males remain in the vicinity of bower sites year round and maintain bowers for about nine to ten months, from May to February, with regular attendance starting at the onset of the wet season in early October. Bowers are abandoned during mid-February to April while their male owners moult. During peak display months adult males average more than 50% of daylight mostly (more than 70%) silently perched on favoured perches within 15 to 20 metres of their bowers. Their remaining time is spent decorating and maintaining the bower, interacting with female visitors or males intent on decoration theft, or visiting bowers of rival males to disrupt their courtship sequences and mating attempts. Bower owners not only aggressively defend their bower site against rival males, but also various other bird species including Black-eared Catbirds, but aggression by adult males away from bowers is rare. Bower-owning males attempt to damage the bowers of neighbouring rivals, and to steal their decorations, including the moss of the short basal maypole column.

Upon detecting a female near his bower a perching male may initially perform simple crest raising display, while rising up on stretched legs to sway side to side. More typically, however, he performs an extra-bower display by leaping rapidly between vertical sapling trunks near his bower whilst occasionally flapping his wings and erecting and fanning his crest. Then he flutters or drops onto his bower mat to hide from the female behind the opposite side of the base of the central maypole. He stands there stiffly with his beak and head pointing up and breast pressed toward the mossy column base and starts a subsong. Then he, while quietly singing, gives brief wing-flicks, while laterally spreading

An unusual, twin-towered and matted, bower of a male Macgregor's Bowerbird, Tari Valley Slopes, Papua New Guinea.

his crest, each time accompanied by a sharp little hop. This sudden movement results in a split second flash of crest colour. At this point in display he may perform a short and brief forward and upward fluttering flight, of some one to two metres high, to immediately return to his take off point.

If sufficiently impressed the female flies down to the mat on the opposite side of the maypole from the male, as he softly sings. She attempts to peer, lean, or move to either side of the maypole to better see him, as he attempts to keep out of her sight by moving around the circular mat. This 'hide and seek' continues until suddenly and rapidly the male alters his elusive behaviour: He fully erects his crest and starts to sway from side to side on extended legs, thus giving the female glimpses of his crest alternately to each side of the maypole. Suddenly he rushes her in an amazingly rapid semi-circular run of mincing steps. This initially often causes the female to flush into adjacent foliage, but if not he rapidly rushes back and past his starting point to then rush at her from the other side of the maypole. He can rapidly repeat this numerous times, alternately from either side of the maypole. His movement is so rapid that, from a distance, he appears as a blurred orange flame swinging repeatedly through a perfect semi-circular arc around one half or more of the bower mat. If she stands her ground in the face of these advances mating occurs.

An adult male Macgregor's Bowerbird attaches more insect frass to the lower sticks of his bower maypole, Tari valley slopes, Papua New Guinea.

Breeding

On Mount Missim birds breed from September to February. Eggs are recorded in nests from October to January, but at Mount Hagen a well-incubated egg was found in early July. Nests are typically placed in pandanus tree crowns, occasionally in saplings or tree fern crowns, two to three metres above ground. Nests are a sparse stick foundation, a leafy cup, and an eggcup lined with supple twiglets and rootlets. Eggs are plain creamy white; 10 single egg clutches average 43 x 28 millimetres. The incubation period is at least 17 days, but the nestling period is unknown. The nestling diet consists of fruits and arthropods, including cicadas and ants.

Status and conservation

This is a common and widespread bird throughout its range, but inconspicuous except for vocal males at bowers. It is extremely abundant at 1200 to 2000 metres on Mt Bosavi, Papua New Guinea. Crests of adult males continue to be worn in the head-dresses of highland men. In October 1999 we found that portable saw mill logging and associated sapling cutting had caused at least four traditional bower sites to be abandoned below Tari Gap, Southern Highlands, Papua New Guinea.

An adult male Macgregor's Bowerbird hides from a visiting female, not visible on the far side of the bower, Tari Valley slopes, Papua New Guinea.

STREAKED BOWERBIRD
Amblyornis subalaris
Etymology: *subalaris* L. under the arms.

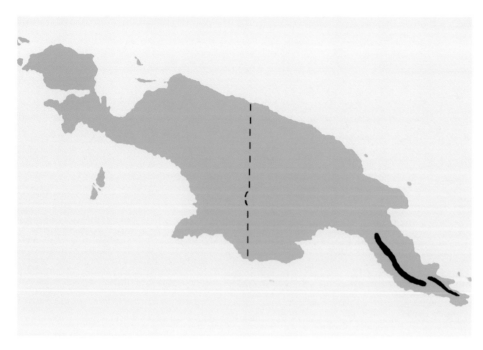

Occupies mountains of southeast New Guinea, from upper Angabunga River in the west to areas of Mount Suckling, Simpson and Moiba to the east; typically at 650 to 1300, rarely to 1500, metres above sea level; thus restricted to Papua New Guinea. The Streaked is replaced at higher altitude by Macgregor's Bowerbird, with which it overlaps infrequently and hybridises with rarely.

Description

A small compact, solid, relatively short-crested, ventrally streaked, inconspicuous gardener bowerbird, except for vocal males at bowers.

24 cm in length: A small, plump, and entirely olive-brown gardener bowerbird that has subtle paler streaking on throat and upper chest that is finer on breast and abdomen. Adult males differ from females and immature males in having a short and broad deep orange crest arising from the mid crown. Bill blackish, eye dark brown; legs blue-grey. Adult females average only fractionally smaller than adult males in size. For pictures of this bowerbird elsewhere see pages 74, 120.

Ecology and habits

Streaked Bowerbirds are usually encountered as lone individuals in primary and taller secondary forests of the lower montane zone, where birds frequent the forest substage up to the canopy. Its vocal repertoire appears similar to that of Macgregor's but requires study. Loud advertisement song is given at bower sites and quieter subsong from bowers during courtship, the latter including vocal avian mimicry, gargles, metallic-sounding clinkings, and twitterings.

Almost nothing is known of the diet, which presumably consists largely of fruits with some insects.

Colour illustration of Streaked Bowerbirds, adult male above and female below, from Sharpe's *Monograph of the Paradiseidae and Ptilonorhynchidae* of 1891-1898 (opposite).

The roofed complex maypole bower of a Streaked Bowerbird, Kagi, Owen Stanley Mountains, Papua New Guinea.

Bowers and courtship

This gardener bowerbird reproduces polygynously, promiscuous males seasonally decorating terrestrial and complex maypole bowers. Traditional bower sites are typically 50 to 75 metres apart, being located on the upper steep slopes of ridges between about five to 30 metres below a forested ridge crest, with secondary growth.

The tepee-shaped bower is based upon a central maypole of sticks built around a thin sapling to about five metres tall, the column comprising of sticks or tree fern fibres. It has a flattened dome-shaped roof, with back and sidewalls, an opening at the front, and a semicircular tunnel-like passageway with an entrance to either side of the central maypole. Bowers reach 80 centimetres tall, 120 centimetres or more wide, and a metre in diameter. Decorations are placed on the outer bower mat and atop the stick parapet before it, often in discrete piles. They include numerous kinds of small blue, purple, mauve, red, yellow, and cream fruits, flowers, and leaves, typically confined to the central column base, and larger colourful fruits, flowers, leaves, and beetle elytra, tree resin, and pieces of fungi on the outer mat and atop the stick parapet before it.

Adult males attend bowers from September to December and one study showed that males are present at their bower sites for at least some 40% of daylight, of which about seven percent is spent at the bower. Males visit bowers of rivals to perform bower destruction and steal decorations.

The courtship display is broadly similar to that of Macgregor's Bowerbird, although it remains to be comprehensively described. Upon detecting a female near his bower a vocally advertising male quickly enters his roofed bower to there give a soft complex subsong. As the female lands on the frontal bower wall and then onto the frontal mat the male's calls becomes quieter. Suddenly he rushes out with crest raised as producing a sharp *pop* followed by a crackling sound; if she remains on the frontal mat in the face of this advance mating occurs.

Breeding

Eggs collected during December to January. One egg was described as yellowish-white; two single egg clutches average 42 x 29 millimetres in size. One nest was a bowl-shaped structure of long brown dead leaves and a few sticks all firmly bound together and lined with twigs. Nest location and situation, nestling care and development, and nesting success rates are unknown.

Status and conservation

Streaked Bowerbirds are locally common throughout their range, but are inconspicuous and infrequently observed away from bowers. Crests of adult males are prized as adornment and trade items by peoples of the Owen Stanley Mountains.

An adult male Streaked Bowerbird beside his decorated central maypole bower base, Kagi, Owen Stanley Mountains, Papua New Guinea.

VOGELKOP BOWERBIRD
Amblyornis inornatus
Etymology: *inornata* unadorned or plain.

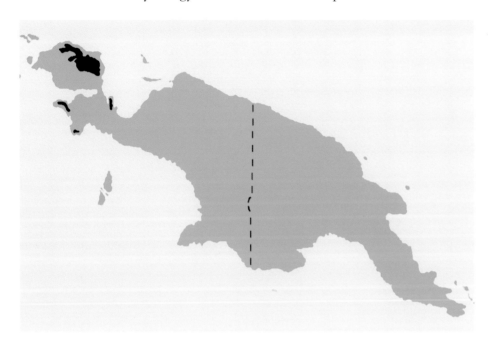

Occurs in the Arfak, Tamrau, Wandammen, Kumawa and Fakfak Mountains of Papua at 1160 to 2000 m on well developed soils; absent from areas with extensive bare karst.

Description

A small, compact, inconspicuous, sexually monomorphic shy bowerbird, with a relatively large head and beak, that builds a most complex bower.

25 cm in length: A small drab species of gardener bowerbird that is dark brownish-olive above and a paler buff or pale cinnamon below in both sexes. Bill blackish and paler at its base, eye dark brown; legs deep bluish. Adult females average fractionally smaller than adult males in weight and size. For pictures of this bowerbird elsewhere see pages 18, 25, 74, 90, 99, 110-111, 119, 122.

Ecology and habits

Birds occur in rainforest with a canopy height of 25 to 30 metres. At low elevations forest habitat is diverse, at middle elevations comprise mainly of *Lithocarpus* oaks and *Casuarina* she-oaks, and at higher elevations mostly of *Nothofagus* beeches.

In flying about bowers birds make a loud wing sound, believed to be purposely. The bower advertisement song repertoire is typical of gardener bowerbirds in including diverse wavering whistles, chugging, wheezing, rasping, coughing, gurgling and spitting sounds, a sharp click, ratchetting sounds, a *kah kah* repeated at intervals and a series of *keu keu keu keu* notes, to name but some. Much vocalisation is superb mimicry, including the songs of many kinds of perching birds, lorikeets and other parrots as well as the sounds of wood

Colour illustration of Vogelkop Bowerbirds, adult male in foreground and female behind, from Sharpe's *Monograph of the Paradiseidae and Ptilonorhynchidae* of 1891-1898 (opposite).

The roofed maypole bower of the Vogelkop Bowerbird, Arfak Mountains, Papua. By and courtesy of Nancy Woodman.

chopping, barking dogs, flapping tarpaulins, generators, and squeaking tripod legs. Males give a quieter subsong, including mimicry, during courtship.

The diet is little known with few records indicating a generalist one of fruits and animals, mostly arthropods.

Bowers and courtship

This bowerbird reproduces polygynously, promiscuous males seasonally decorating complex terrestrial maypole bowers. Favoured bower sites are on ridge spines and flanks with sloping ground. The remains of old and disused bower structures within a few metres of actively used ones indicate many bower sites are traditional.

While crestless adult males look just like females throughout the mountains occupied by this bowerbird their maypole bowers and decoration take on two distinctive forms; those on the Tamrau, Arfak, and Wandammen Mountains are typically roofed and hut-like, fundamentally like those of Streaked Bowerbirds, while those on the Fakfak and Kumawa Mountains are simple and roofless and thus fundamentally like those of Macgregor's Bowerbird. The basis of both bower types is a central column of sticks about a vertial sapling trunk. Hut-like bowers are clearly an elaborated, roofed, form of the basic maypole type bower such as Macgregor's builds, but in which the uppermost column is expanded outward and downward to form a roof with contiguous walls except for a large frontal entrance aperture. The roof is typically of epiphytic orchids stems, but in some cases involves sticks or ferns, and the column base is covered with moss and extended down and out to form a frontal mat or lawn.

Towers of the more simplistic maypole type bowers on the Fakfak and Kumawa Mountains are built around saplings up to six metres tall, and their towers reach up to two metres high. The near perfectly circular flat moss mat about the tower base may be up to two metres in diameter. Bower decorations, their colour and quantity vary considerably between localities. Mats are decorated with discrete piles of colourful fruits and flowers, insect exoskeletons, pieces of charcoal, fungi, and other items that may include butterflies, beetles, acorns, bark pieces, feathers, and the amber-like resin of pandanus trees.

Males on the Kumawa Mountains apparently paint some bower decorations with oily excrement, but this requires further study. As in other bowerbirds, younger males build inadequate structures, and have fewer decorations that are often of inappropriate colours. Bowers are attended and well decorated from July to February, but months of peak activity vary across the range of the species. During the display season males typically spend 50% or more of their day perched within 20 metres of, and four to 20 metres above, their bowers. Fights and chases between individuals within and about bowers occur. Bower owners also chase other bird species, up to their own size, from their bower sites. Bower destruction and decoration theft is common.

A bower-owning male immediately responds to the arrival of a female by

An unusual bower of the Vogelkop Bowerbird made of primitive ferns, Hungku, Anggi Lakes. By Will Betz.

rushing into the rear of his bower to crouch, hiding, behind decorations while producing a song that includes vocal mimicry. He stands stiff and erect and occasionally runs out from concealment to the bower entrance with his head cocked to one side as if listening, or looking, for a few moments before dashing back inside. His singing is constant throughout this display. Of 16 males studied at their Arfak Mountains bowers only half mated, the three most successful individuals performing 60% of all matings. These more successful males built larger bowers and had more blue items decorating them than did less successful males.

The simple maypole bower type of the population of the Vogelkop Bowerbird on the Fafak Mountains, Papua. By Will Betz.

Breeding

Two nests, each containing a single whitish egg, were found; one near Hungku, Anggi Lakes in May and the other above Mokwam, Arfak Mountains, at 1430 metres, in early October 1994. Both were built into forking branches of a sparsely foliaged sapling, at one and two-and-a-half metres above ground. One was a rather untidy structure of sticks with a lining of leaves, rather like nests of Macgregor's but with fewer sticks about the base. The two eggs averaged 41 x 29 millimetres in size. Incubation, nestling period, and nestling care and development are unknown. Three females were in breeding condition during September.

Status and conservation

This is a common bird throughout its range, being inconspicuous except for vocal males at bowers. People near Hatam, in the Arfak Mountains traditionally took care never to destroy bowers.

A male Vogelkop Bowerbird trims the ends of the sticks above his bower entrance, Mokwam, Arfak Mountains. By Will Betz.

YELLOW-FRONTED BOWERBIRD
Amblyornis flavifrons
Etymology: *flavifrons* L. *flavus*, golden-yellow; *frons*, forehead or brow.

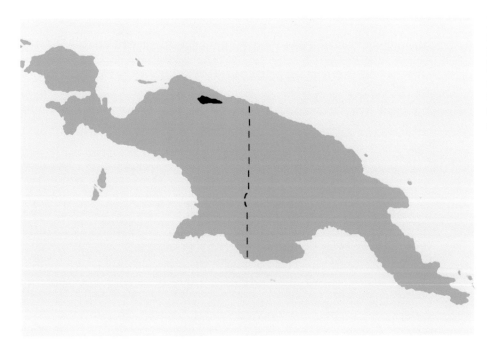

Found only on the Foja, or Gauttier, Mountains of Papua between 940 and at least 2000, but mostly above 1100, metres above sea level. Adult males rarely occur below 1600 metres and bowers only between 1650 and 1800 metres.

Description

A large, compact, and solid gardener bowerbird only on the Foja Mountains, Papua, where inconspicuous except for large and strikingly crested and vocal adult males at bowers.

24 cm. A large, relatively short tailed, gardener bowerbird species entirely brownish-olive above and rich buff richly washed deep cinnamon below. Adult males differ from females and immature males in having an extensive, broad, erectile orange-yellow crest that extends from the base of the beak to the mantle. Bill blackish, eye dark brown; legs bluish-grey. For pictures of this bowerbird elsewhere see pages 78, 87, 90, 118, 120, 186.

Ecology and habits

Birds live in montane moss forest, dominated above 1900 metres by oak tree species of *Araucaria*, *Nothofagus*, *Podocarpus*, and *Lithocarpus*, and frequent the middle storey and lower canopy between six and 20 metres above ground but occasionally visit the forest floor. Bower advertisement song is diverse, loud and weird, including avian and other mimicry. Calls include short high nasal screeches, rasps, clucks, wheezes, croaks, crackling sounds, whip like sounds, and others like the sound of shovelling gravel, crumpling paper, striking a tree trunk, suddenly letting the breath out, and clicking the tongue against the palate. A

Colour illustration of adult male Yellow-fronted (lower) and Macgregor's (upper) Bowerbirds from Sharpe's *Monograph of the Paradiseidae and Ptilonorhynchidae* of 1891-1898 (opposite).

203

The simple maypole bower of the Yellow-fronted Bowerbird, Foja Mountains, Papua. By and courtesy of Steve Richards (opposite).

An adult male Yellow-fronted Bowerbird looks for bower decoration on the leaf litter beside his bower, Foja Mountains, Papua. By and courtesy of Bruce M. Beehler.

quite subsong, including mimicry, is given during courtship. Other than that fruits are snatched from trees and carried off, nothing is known of the diet.

Bowers and courtship

Presumed to reproduce polygynously, with promiscuous males seasonally decorating a simple terrestrial maypole bower and females building and attending nests alone. Bower sites are on ridge crests about half a kilometre apart. The bower is based about the vertical trunk of a living sapling or tree fern trunk, much like that of Macgregor's Bowerbird. Sticks are piled about the central trunk to form a tower of up to about a metre high. A basal circular moss mat with a raised outer rim, about a metre in diameter, encircles the central tower and the immediately adjacent forest floor is cleared of debris. Decorations include discrete piles of blue, green, and yellow fruits each on a distinct part of the circular mat.

Only one display was observed, when two birds were at a bower: An

Adult male Yellow-fronted Bowerbirds have a more extensive crest than all other gardener bowerbirds, Foja Mountains, Papua. By and courtesy of Bruce M. Beehler.

adult male was holding a blue fruit for 20 minutes in his bill, about a third the size of his head, and producing a loud sound like that caused by a large mammal walking on loose gravel before displaying to the presumed female. When she appeared he flew to a horizontal perch near his bower, gave a weak high-pitched two-note whistle, and then remained silent there for the rest of his display. She periodically shifted perches at two to 10 metres high, remaining about 10 metres from him, sometimes vertically above him. As she changed perches he turned to face her and thus direct the blue fruit at her. When she was overhead he directed his body vertically upward and when she flew to the understorey he orientated his body horizontally toward her. Often he spread his crest laterally, raised and lowered it vertically, and shook his head rapidly side to side causing his crest to quiver. When she flew off he resumed loud calling and then flew off too.

Breeding

Nothing is known about nest location and situation, nest structure and building, eggs and incubation, or nestling care and development.

Status and conservation

This bowerbird is geographically extremely limited. The total Foja Mountains population is estimated at a few thousand or less. As only the above meagre information is known about this bowerbird, the adult male appearance of which suggests a most close relationship with Archbold's Bowerbird, further biological range, population, and status knowledge is urgently required and genetic material eagerly awaited.

An adult male Yellow-fronted Bowerbird, displaying a fruit in his beak, stands at the base of his simple maypole bower, Foja Mountains, Papua. By and courtesy of Bruce M. Beehler

ARCHBOLD'S BOWERBIRD

Archboldia papuensis

Etymology: *Archboldia* after Richard Archbold (1907-76), Research Associate in Mammalogy, American Museum of Natural History. *papuensis* after Papua, or New Guinea.

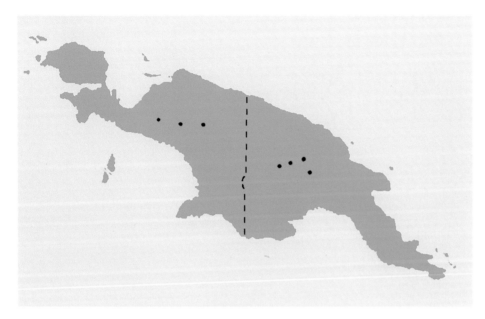

Patchily distributed along the New Guinea central mountain ranges at 1700 to 2800, but exceptionally to 3700, metres above sea level. In Papua birds occur in the Wissel Lakes area, Ilaga Valley, Bele River, Lake Habbema and north slopes of the Oranje Mountains. In Papua New Guinea they are recorded on Mount Giluwe, southwest and south slopes of Mount Hagen, Tari Gap, and the southern Karius Range.

Description

A solid, inconspicuously shy bowerbird of montane New Guinea moss forests immediately above forests inhabited by Macgregor's Bowerbird. This species includes two geographical forms, or subspecies; see page 291.

35 to 37 cm. A large, long-tailed, bowerbird that is all black except for a few feathers smudged with cinnamon in females and young males to a small discrete patch of pure cinnamon on the leading wing edge in adult males. Adult males also differ from females and immature males in being blacker and in having an extensive, finely-tapering, brilliant yellow crest streaked with black and arising from the base of the beak and extending onto the nape. Bill black, eye dark brown; legs dark blue-grey. Adult females are lighter and smaller in size than adult males. For pictures of this bowerbird elsewhere see pages 37, 75, 83, 96, 100, 103, 141.

Ecology and habits

Sparse, but possibly locally common, in frost-prone high montane mossy *Nothofagus* beech forest with coniferous *Podocarpus* tree species in the canopy, and pandanus and *Schefflera* umbrella trees and scrambling bamboo on gentle topography.

The repertoire of male bower advertisement calls is varied, ventriloqual, and includes mimicry, loud hollow sounds and whistles, buzzing, snapping,

An adult male Archbold's Bowerbird arrives on one of his bower perches with a decoration for his bower mat, Tari Gap, Papua New Guinea (opposite).

209

tearing sounds, harsh, grating, or churring notes. A commonly mimicked sound is that of bird wings vigorously and loudly fluttered and a cicada-like call is apparently mimicry of these insects. Calls of at least 10 bird species that occur in this bowerbird's habitat are reproduced well. Mimicry of characteristic inanimate sounds include those of pandanus fronds rattling against each other and the sound of them falling and hitting the ground. A characteristic note that is also given away from bowers is a loud harsh *waagh* often immediately repeated once and a distinctive unpleasant down slurred *sherrd* note given once or twice.

Next to nothing known of the diet of adult birds but fruits and animals, mostly insects and tree-climbing lizards, are fed to nestlings.

Bowers and courtship

Archbold's Bowerbird reproduces polygynously; the promiscuous males seasonally decorating terrestrial maypole bowers. Traditional bower sites are dispersed through suitable habitat. In our Tari Gap study area the nearest neighbour distance between 16 traditional bower sites averaged 370 metres over 1000 hectares. One active bower site persisted for at least 15 years. Fidelity to a single court site by individual adult males is high, one individual attending the same site for at least six seasons. Immature males establish rudimentary, temporary, bowers near long-established ones of adult males.

An Archbold's Bowerbird's bower with King of Saxony Bird of Paradise plumes on its central bower mat, Tari Gap, Papua New Guinea.

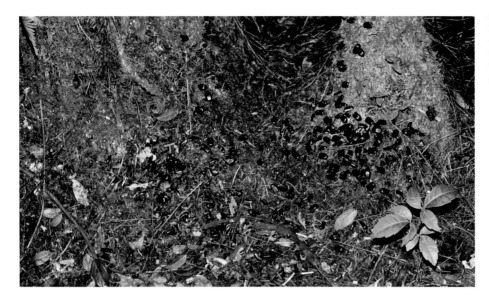

Detail of part of an Archbold's Bowerbird's bower mat, showing discrete piles of black beetle wing cases as decorations, Tari Gap, Papua New Guinea.

Adult males typically renovate and add to their bower at the beginning of each season, on the same spot, mat, and perches. At Tari Gap this happens during September to December but on Mount Hagen bowers are attended as early as July. Bower etablishment involves the clearing of an area, beneath a number of prerequisite perches, that then has fern fronds laid upon it to form the mat. Perches above are draped with innumerable orchids stems, older ones being overlaid with new ones to become brown-yellow with time. Many recently placed orchids may have flowers on them. Orchid stems are not decorations, however, but constitute arboreal bower material. Bower mats are variable and irregular in shape, some being roughly oval or circular whilst others are roughly rectangular, square, or triangular, and may cover an area up to six by five metres. The orchid-draped and decorated branches may reach up to two and a half metres above the mat.

Decorations are often placed upon the bower mat in discrete aggregations. The mat of a larger bower is typically decorated with discrete piles of at least some large snail shells, beetle wing cases, fruits, fungus, tree resin, and charcoal. Several close to a road also may have pieces of brown beer bottle glass on them. The most impressively rare decorations are head plumes of adult male King of Saxony Birds of Paradise. We found between one and six of these peculiar feathers on each of only the six largest of 24 bowers. Thus these male bowerbirds use extravagant plumes of a bird of paradise to impress females of their own kind! As male King of Saxony Birds of Paradise do not acquire adult plumage until five to seven years old, and then wear only two such plumes it can be appreciated how rare a bower decoration these feathers represent. Presumably males with this decoration on their bower have a greater chance of successful courtship than rivals lacking them; a situation found to be true of Satin Bowerbirds with parrot feathers, see Chapters 2, 3 and 6.

During periods of peak display adult males at Tari Gap average more than

An adult male Archbold's Bowerbird performs the 'grovelling' prostrate courtship posture on his bower mat, Tari Gap, Papua New Guinea (opposite above).

An adult male Archbold's Bowerbird performs the head-raised courtship posture on his bower mat, Tari Gap, Papua New Guinea (opposite below).

An adult male Archbold's Bowerbird adds a fresh fern frond to his bower mat, Tari Gap, Papua New Guinea.

50% of daylight present at their courts, mostly (more than 60%) singing from perches immediately above the bower to a radius of about 12 to 15 metres. Their remaining time is spent maintaining the bower, displaying with or without a female present, and chasing other males or other birds from their bower site. Decoration theft probably occurs because we found that King of Saxony Bird of Paradise plumes often disappeared from bowers between our visiting them.

Male advertisement vocalizations become more frequent, intense, and then softer shortly prior to the discernable presence of a female near the bower. By the time she is on a bower perch the male drops onto his mat to display: He lowers his sleeked body to press his throat, lower beak, breast, abdomen, and tail into the mat with his wings close to their normal position. The crest is slightly fanned and fore-crown feathering erected and spread as he utters a continuous subsong. If she drops onto the mat he rushes at her in a ritualised aggressive way to chase her with loud calls to or just beyond the mat edge. He then prostrates himself again and may repeat the process several times to entice her back. If she remains away from the mat, however, the prostrate male shuffles over it in a grovelling manner. Upon her return his crest is presented to her as he shakes his repeatedly raised and lowered head. Suddenly the last of his, increasingly rapid, head-lifts raises his entire body to hop onto the female to mate. During this courtship a quieter subsong, including a continuous murmuring or bleating call interspersed

with hissing, chugging, spluttering, and notes like the sound of dripping water and lip-smacking, mimicry of other bird calls, the sound of whirring bird wings, and fluttering vegetation, is given by the male.

Breeding

Breeding occurs during September to February. Until we discovered the first nest and egg at Tari Gap in November 1987 the nesting biology was unknown, and in 1988 and 1989 we found eight more active nests there. Nests containing eggs were mostly during late November to December. Females nest in the leafy crown of a sapling at three to seven metres above ground within, or adjacent to, a small gap in the forest with no canopy directly above and thus isolated from adjacent vegetation. Nesting like this may reduce the chances of potential predation by tree-climbing predators. A female may habitually nest in the same area, sometimes the same tree, over consecutive years. Seven active nests averaged 250 metres from an active traditional bower.

The nest is an untidy deep, bulky, bowl that is possibly larger than those of other bowerbirds proportionate to the female. It consists of a stick foundation, a deep substantial cup of large dried leaves with uppermost ones fresh and green, and an eggcup lining of curved twiglets. Eggs are a pale buff with slight gloss, unmarked save for inconspicuous, tiny, irregular, sparse, slightly darker spots. Eggs of six single-egg clutches average 47 x 31 millimetres. The incubation period is 26 to 27 days and the long nestling period averages 30 days.

Over 70% of the nestling diet is fruit and the remainder animals, including tree-climbing lizards (skinks), beetles, cicadas, and occasional pieces of nestling birds. Females cease brooding their nestlings after they reach 15 days old. They chase other birds from their nest area, including their own kind, and have not been heard to give mimicry. The overall success rate of eight nests was 88% and the average number of young produced per female each season was one.

Status and conservation

This relatively rare bowerbird is classified as 'lower risk/near threatened' by BirdLife International's global review of threatened birds in 2000. However, as much suitable habitat remains intact Archbold's Bowerbird cannot be considered under threat in Papua New Guinea or Papua. Should future large-scale logging involve its habitat things could change rapidly, however, with respect to its status. Upon returning to Tari Gap in 1999, having studied there over the previous decade, we found that fire following a severe drought 20 months previously, plus disturbance caused by the harvesting of pandanus fruits and associated human activity, resulted in at least six traditional bower sites being abandoned. Increased human population and associated habitat degradation perhaps pose potential threats to this bird in the longer term. A meaningful survey of this bowerbird is badly needed.

A female Archbold's Bowerbird carries fruits in her mouth and throat to her offspring Tari Gap, Papua New Guinea (opposite).

GOLDEN BOWERBIRD

Prionodura newtoniana
Etymology: *Prionodura* Gr. *prionodes*, serrated; *oura*, tail. *newtoniana* after the
ornithologist Alfred Newton (1829-1907).

Confined to upland rainforests of the Australian Wet Tropics of the Atherton Region, Queensland, from Thornton Range and Mount Windsor Tableland in north to the Seaview-Paluma Ranges in the south. Birds occur at 350 to 1530, but more typically 680 to 1260, metres above sea level. During winter some female-plumaged individuals move to lower altitudes.

Description

The smallest bowerbird, less stocky than others, adult males with a relatively long forked tail. It is an inconspicuous and relatively quite species save males at bowers.

23 to 25 cm. A small, relatively slender, maypole-building bowerbird. Females and immature males are generally brownish-olive above and a much paler, glaucous, below with paler chin and throat and darker, slightly brownish, sides of breast and flanks. Adult males differ radically from females in having a much longer and forked tail and in being an olive-green richly suffused with deep golden yellow that is contrasted by a large pale glossy orange-yellow nape patch and entire underparts. The entire glossy body plumage reflects pure white highlights, like spun glass. Bill blackish-brown with a paler tip and base; eye pale, more so in adult males; legs blue-grey with an olive wash. This bowerbird shows the greatest disparity between adult male and adult female tail lengths. These, and their relative proportions, reflect sexual selection upon males for flight courtship display traits. Adult females are heavier than adult males. For pictures of this bowerbird elsewhere see pages 10-11, 14, 15, 16, 17, 38, 58, 75, 82, 95, 97, 106, 151, 292.

Illustration of Golden Bowerbirds, adult male above and female below, from Sharpe's *Monograph of the Paradiseidae and Ptilonorhynchidae* of 1891-1898 (opposite).

A tall single-towered bower of an adult male Golden Bowerbird, from which the display perch protrudes from one side, Paluma Range, north Queensland.

Ecology and habits

Birds bathe and drink in shallow creek pools, and also drink from water-filled tree cavities and droplets on leaf litter and foliage. They also foliage-bathe by flying into wet foliage and fluttering and hovering amongst it. Individuals 'ant' themselves by wiping the insects held in the bill tip down the length of their wing and tail feathers to maintain their plumage and deter parasites. When direct sunlight strikes them they will adopt a sunning posture, with erect breast, rump, head, and nape feathers, down-pressed tail, and drooped wings.

Bower advertisement song of adult males consists of a pulsating rattle note, typically lasting one or two seconds, repeated several times. Other calls by males at bowers consist of single squeal, screech, scold-rasp, or wolf whistle notes or a medley of them. Males also produce high-quality mimicry, involving not only calls of more than 20 other bird species but also mechanical sounds.

We found some individual adult males living for more than 23 years. Two males wore adult plumage for 16 to 17 years. Immature males wear female plumage for at least five to six years before attaining adult plumage. Some immatures wear a discernible subadult plumage, with some yellow feathers in otherwise female-like plumage, the season before attaining full adult plumage.

Golden Bowerbirds eat fruits and animals, mostly insects, but predominantly the former and they take a wide variety of plants' fruits as well as some flowers and buds. Foraging mainly occurs in the lower canopy and subcanopy. Almost 90% of fruit eating involves drupes and berries, but some capsular fruits are eaten. A large proportion of the fruit eaten is taken from vines. Fruits are mostly searched for among foliage but many, especially vine fruits, are taken by sallying and occasionally hovering. Males cache fruits in tree trunk crevices, dead tree stumps, among leaf litter and beneath fallen timber, around bower sites; most commonly bunches of wild peppers. We also watched a nesting female retrieve a fruit from a cache. Birds usually forage alone but three or four may simultaneously visit a fruiting canopy, sometimes with Black-eared Catbirds, Tooth-billed and Satin Bowerbirds, and other fruit eating birds, without aggressive interaction. Animal foods include caterpillars, termites, cicadas, beetles, and spiders; being mostly foraged for in the lower canopy and subcanopy. Cicadas may be hawked and chased, and then eaten on the ground.

Bowers and courtship

Golden Bowerbirds reproduce polygynously, the promiscuous males decorating vast maypole type bowers. Traditional bower sites are dispersed throughout suitable topography. Favoured sites are on flatter terrain and along ridge slopes, on gentle slopes and ridges immediately around hillcrests, and below steeper slopes where terrain levels off, with canopy vegetation coverage of usually more than 70%. In our 50 hectare study area on the Paluma Range, north Queensland, the average distance between 12 traditional sites was 150 metres, one to each 4.2 hectares. Twenty-one of 25 traditional sites were regularly attended for 20 consecutive seasons. The average home range size of eight adult males was seven hectares. Traditional adult male bower owners attend one site for an average of seven years, but up at least 16 years. One male Golden wore immature plumage for at least five years and then took over a traditional bower site in his first year in adult plumage to then occupy the site for at least 16 years.

From five to two years before attaining traditional bower ownership, we found that immature males visited many bowers of other males at an average of almost 400 metres from the one they eventually come to occupy. The year before attaining full bower site occupancy this average distance was halved. During this period of wider movements immature males may establish rudimentary, smaller, less well decorated and temporary bowers at sites near traditional ones. As they grow older males increasingly restrict such visitations to only several adjacent traditional bowers, until subsequently visiting only but two or three. They subsequently attempt to focus their attention upon one adjacent traditional bower site. If persistent there, in the face of competition by their older neighbours, such males may eventually come to take over the adjacent traditional bower site, usually in their first year of adult plumage.

Traditional bowers are single or twin towers of sticks. A tower may reach two metres tall. Towers are built around, and supported by, saplings, vines, or trees. The sticks of the bower become firmly fused together by the action of a fungus that is ubiquitous in the habitat. Each bower has a pre-existing horizontal display perch consisting of a woody vine, living sapling, fallen dead branch, or a tree root. This bower perch protrudes from a single tower bower, or connects twin towers. Uncommonly, one or both towers may be arboreal with their bower perch up to two metres above ground. Where they abut the bower perch, tower sticks are tightly aligned to form a discrete platform or platforms, upon which bower decorations are placed.

New bowers start as small single arboreal conical or maypole-shaped structures and do not reach full size until after two to three seasons of construction. The frequent use of one or more perches about bower sites results in males placing, or leaving, sticks at the point they diverge from the tree trunk. Such sticks accumulate, become fused by fungus, and thus develop into arboreal or terrestrial subsidiary structures. We discovered that the average minimum 'life' of traditional bower structures is about nine years, but some exist for in excess of 20 years. Bower replacement may be due to general deterioration, including the collapse of a tower support or bower perch, tree fall, or mammal damage. A replacement bower averages 14 metres from the previously actively used one. Only one main bower structure is actively decorated at any bower site during any one season.

Bower decorations are mainly grey-green lichen and sprigs of creamy-white fruit with an attached black seed of a *Melicope* shrub, but creamy-white flowers of orchids, jasmine, and silky oaks and small green-yellow fruits are sometimes used. Most decorations are harvested from the habitat or stolen from the bowers of rival males. A twin-towered bower often has only beard lichen to one side of its bower perch and seedpods to the other. When males visit bowers of rival

An adult male Golden Bowerbird on his central bower perch, with decorations on the platform at the base of each tower, Paluma Range, north Queensland.

males in order to gain experience or to steal decorations they invariably do so in the owner's absence. If the owner is present he usually aggressively chases the intruder off his bower.

Seasonally regular attendance of traditional bower sites typically starts during July to August and terminates in January when wet season rains start, but varies year to year in response to climate and resultant food abundance. If rains ease there may be a brief period of post-moult activity during March to early May.

During the peak display season adult males we studied average more than 60% of daylight at their bower site. Seasonal variation in time invested at bowers varies from year to year subject to weather conditions, particularly excessive drought, and resultant food availability. Males on the Paluma Range spent 63% of daytime at bowers during a climatically normal season but only 36% during an excessively dry one. The average distance males travel from bowers to forage and collect bower decorations averaged 88 metres; but to steal decorations from rival males' bowers they travelled an average of 195 metres, to as far as 490 metres.

Males spend more than 80% of their time perched silently above or about their bower. The remaining time is spent in giving advertisememt *rattles* and

other calls, maintaining and decorating the bower, and in chasing or displaying to visitors. Females may be repeatedly chased from the bower perch, these chases interspersed with brief displays accompanied by medley calls involving mimicry. Displacement chasing is not just directed at other Golden Bowerbirds but also at other small birds that land on the bower.

Males perform at least five basic courtship display elements: *Chase, Bow, Head nod and shake, Flight/hover,* and *Hiding*. Upon seeing a female within his bower site an adult male does not approach her but gives some squeals, screeches, and vocal mimicry and performs *Head nod and shake* and *Bow* displays followed by one or more *Flight/hover* displays. The male then moves up to 20 metres away from his bower to perch and perform a *Hiding* display accompanied by a soft subsong that includes high quality mimicry. The male hides behind a tree trunk or branch. Once a female is settled on his bower perch the male suddenly stops vocalizing and drops down close to the forest floor, sometimes onto it, to perform a brief serpentine run of several metres to then make an indirect, rapid, silent flight through foliage to surprise the female by aggressively *Chasing* her from his bower with loud calls. This behaviour may be repeated with each return of the visitor to the bower perch, with display elements other than *Hiding* possibly occurring at any time and in any order. All of the five display elements

An immature male Golden Bowerbird visits a bower of one of his elders, Paluma Range, north Queensland (above left).

Adult male Golden Bowerbirds spend much time perched above their bowers, singing and watching for visitors, Paluma Range, north Queensland (above right).

A softly singing adult male Golden Bowerbird peers round a tree at a visiting female during the hiding phase of his courtship, Paluma Range, north Queenland.

are probably performed during successful courtship, perhaps in a typical sequence but as no matings are reported, this requires confirmation.

Breeding

Breeding occurs from September to February, with egg laying peaking November to December, and nestlings in nests during December to January. On average nesting lasts four months, but varies with location, altitude, and weather. In an exceptionally dry season all nests we observed failed to produce young, apparently due to the lack of food. Nest sites are mostly located on flat to slightly sloping ground although some occur on steeper slopes, sometimes near creeks. The same females may repeatedly use nesting locations, even specific sites. Thirty-seven active nests on the Paluma Range averaged 97 metres from an active traditional bower, some being midway between two or more active bowers.

GOLDEN BOWERBIRD

Nests are deep, bulky, open cups typically built within a 'roofed' vertical crevice in a tree trunk or in a crevice-like situation. Nests are usually about one-and-a-half metres above ground, but may be as high as five metres. The nest has a stick foundation: This forms an irregular platform beneath and around the lower nest of a discrete substantial bowl-shaped structure of dead leaves and leaf skeletons and, within this, an eggcup lining of fine supple and springy tendrils. Nests take up to 25 days to construct. Whilst most nests are laid within two weeks of completion, some are not laid in for four weeks after it. Eggs are plain whitish or off-white; 116 eggs average 35 x 25 millimetres. One to three eggs are laid but most clutches are of two (76% of 67). At two nests the eggs of two-egg clutches were laid on alternate days. Eggs may hatch on the same or subsequent days, up to 23 hours apart. The incubation period is 21 to 23 days and nestling period 17 to 20 days. Females cease brooding nestlings of a brood of two after they are nine days old, and after 13 days in the case of a single nestling. The overall nestling feeding rate, and the number of meals provided per hour, is greater for broods of two than for broods of one.

The nestling diet is nearly 70% fruit and the remainder animals, particularly insects. Whole or part cicadas form the majority of the nestling animal diet but beetles, orthopterons, termites, other insects and their larvae also feature. A female will catch a larger insect and reduce it to pieces near the nest, returning to it repeatedly until it is all fed to her brood. The proportion of fruit in the diet increases with nestling age. Juveniles that have left the nest are also fed on fruit or insect foods.

Females may not mimic as their nests are approached by a potential predator, but will perform a distraction display by flying to the ground and, with drooped wings held out on the ground, 'hobble' away. Black-eared Catbirds probably eat Golden Bowerbird eggs and nestlings. We once saw a female Golden approaching her nest suddenly adopt a completely static 'frozen' posture and remain silent on her perch for several minutes as a catbird called and moved above her nest. We found the overall success of 29 nests was 28%, the average number of fledged young produced per female in each season averaging one. There is no evidence of two broods being successfully raised in a single season.

Status and conservation

This is a common bird throughout its limited remaining, but fully protected, range. It is generally inconspicuous except for vocal and animated males about bowers. This bowerbird remains as stable and well protected as any other bird endemic to the Australian Wet Tropics. Given the national park, plus world heritage, status of the entire extensive remaining upland habitat of this bird it is in no way threatened or endangered – unless by the indirect effects of global warming upon its habitat and ecology at some future time.

MASKED BOWERBIRD

Sericulus aureus
Etymology: *Sericulus* dim. of L. *sericum*, silk (Gr. *serikos*, silken). *aureus* L. *aurum* golden or gold.

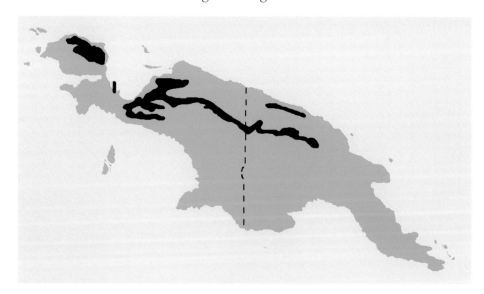

The north New Guinea ranges of the Vogelkop, Wandammen, Weyland, Oranje, Torricelli and Prince Alexander Mountains, central and north Coastal Range, east to near the Sepik River, at 850 to 1400 metres above sea level. Single adult males have been seen near Wara Hill, at 500 metres, Ruti National Park, Jimi Valley, Papua New Guinea. This species hybridises with the Flame Bowerbird on the Wataikwa River, south Papua.

Description

A small, relatively slight, and little known retiringly shy bowerbird that is inconspicuous unless heard and seen at bowers.

24 to 25 cm in length: A larger species of silky bowerbird with females and immature males generally olive-brown above and orange-yellow below but with the chin, throat, and upper breast washed with the olive-brown. Adult males are a brilliant flame orange on crown, nape, and mantle to brilliant deep yellow on wings and all underparts. The facial mask, leading wing edges and tips, tail and thighs are jet black. Bill blackish, with a pale blue-grey base in adult males; eye dark brown in females and immature males, pale lemon yellow in adult males; legs greyish. Adult females weigh less than males but are otherwise similar in size but have a longer tail. For pictures of this bowerbird elsewhere see pages 2, 20, 112.

Ecology and habits

When not at the bower, this is an active but shy bird of forest foliage that typically forages alone or, possibly more frequently in winter, in small groups; moving between about ten metres above ground to the treetops in twos or threes. Silent away from bowers except for occasional faint *ksh* notes, and a small but harshly rasped note. Little is known of vocalisations at bowers.

The diet includes fruits and insects. Birds take figs and will forage in tree canopies with Vogelkop Bowerbirds and other frugivores, including fruit-doves and birds of paradise, without interaction. A female-plumaged individual fed in a canopy among a mixed species flock.

Illustration of Masked Bowerbirds, adult male above and female below, from Sharpe's *Monograph of the Paradiseidae and Ptilonorhynchidae* of 1891-1898 (opposite).

Bowers and courtship

Reproduces polygynously, the promiscuous males seasonally building and decorating terrestrial avenue bowers. Little is known about bower locations and sites; a few bowers have been located along ridge tops: One was in a densely forested area, lacking grassland, beneath tall trees with a moderately open canopy. Another was beneath a stand of bamboo. An Arfak Mountains bower, some 1220 metres above sea level, was similar to that of the Regent Bowerbird, but a little larger and with straight walls and no decorations. A Tamrau Mountains bower, at about 1100 to 1300 metres, was atop a moderately sloping rounded ridge with steep sides on the northwest face of the highest peak for at least 78^2 kilometres. The area was densely forested, lacking grassland, and the bower was beneath tall trees with a moderately open canopy. Two bowers above Tanah Merah were near a ridge top clearing at 870 metres and another was at 910 metres on the same ridge.

Arfak and Tamrau Mountains bowers are active during August to November. One Tamrau Mountains bower was 18 centimetres along its central avenue and 26 centimetres from the ground to the top sticks. Bower decorations are few with up to only six being observed. These include blue and purple fruits, black bracket fungus, snail shells, and yellow to bronze leaves of various sizes. Once, blue berries disappeared from a bower but it was not known if they had been stolen by rival males or eaten by Black-eared Catbirds, which have been observed taking fruits from a bower and eating them elsewhere.

One male attended his Arfak Mountains bower for periods averaging ten minutes, and ranging from two to 30 minutes at the peak of bower construction. Most bower attendance was during 0730 to 0830 and 1000 to 1100 hours, with only a couple of afternoon visits during 1330 to 1600 hours. Clear sunny mornings resulted in most attendance during September to November. Adult males intensively paint the inside of their bower walls.

A rare photograph of an adult male Masked Bowerbird at his bower, Arfak Mountains, Papua. By and courtsey of Mike Potts.

Courtship is little known other than that one adult male displayed toward his bower avenue entrance, apparently in the absence of another bird, during September to November. Display postures involved turning the head and bill away from the bower, much as Regent Bowerbirds do, while drooping and partly opening the wing to the same side that the head is turned, and pulling the partly fanned tail toward the head as male grey, and particularly Fawn-breasted, bowerbirds do. Wing flicks, leaps, and serpentine head movements much like those of Regent, Spotted, and Western Bowerbirds, are also performed. Males present a decoration to a visiting female and may nudge the sticks at one end of an avenue wall, as do grey bowerbirds. An odd buzzing vocalization is sometimes given during display.

Breeding

Nothing is known about nest location and situation, nest structure and building, eggs and incubation, and nestling care and development.

Status and conservation

Not an uncommon bird in hill and mid-montane forests of the Vogelkop, and north slopes of the Snow Mountains near Mount Wilhelmina. The presence of dried trade skins at Goroka in Papua New Guinea indicate a geographically extensive trade, until at least as recently as the 1970s, that probably persists today.

An avenue bower of the Masked Bowerbird, decorated with blue fruits, Arfak Mountains, Papua. By and courtesy of Mike Potts.

FLAME BOWERBIRD

Sericulus ardens
Etymology: *ardens* L. glowing or burning [flaming].

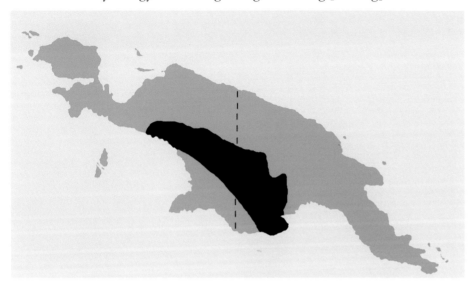

Patchily distributed in the lowlands and foothills of the southern New Guinea watershed from the southwest (Wataikwa-Mimika, upper Noord-Endrich River, Papua) eastward to the upper Fly River (Kiunga, Black River), Strickland-Nomad River and east to Mount Bosavi, up to about 760 metres above sea level. It also occurs in the Tarara-Morehead area and apparently also inland from Merauke, between Kumbe and the Merauke River. This species hybridises with the Masked Bowerbird on the Wataikwa River, south Papua.

Description

Similar in size, character, and presumably biology, to the Masked Bowerbird.

25 to 26 cm in length: More reddish-orange above, slightly smaller and shorter-tailed than the Masked Bowerbird Adult males entirely lack black facial mask feathering, this area being rich flame orange as is the rest of the head, nape, and mantle. Bill brownish, eye dark brown in females and immature males, bright yellow in adult males; legs blackish. Sexes similar in size other than adult females having a longer tail than adult males. Weights unrecorded. For pictures of this bowerbird elsewhere see pages 8, 127 157.

Ecology and habits

Birds frequent rainforests and tall secondary forests, including forest patches in flat savanna, mainly beneath *Melaleuca* in the Trans-Fly area. An uncommon and shy species of the canopy and mid-canopy, but birds like to perch on exposed emergent branches. The little known vocal repertoire includes harsh rasping and hissing notes, and an oft-repeated churring *shh* or a faint *ksh* note. Fruits and insects are eaten but no further details exist. Birds apparently forage singly, sometimes in twos or threes, and occasionally in company of other fruit-eating birds in the same plants.

Bowers and courtship

Reproduces polygynously, the promiscuous males seasonally building and decorating terrestrial avenue bowers. Little is known about the traditional status of bower sites and their locations. A few bowers have been found on gently sloping ground in foothill, swamp, and tall secondary forest with sparse

Illustration of Flame Bowerbirds, adult male above and female below, from the British ornithological journal *Ibis,* Jubilee Supplement 2, of 1915.

A bower built by an adult male Flame Bowerbird in captivity, in Qatar.

undergrowth and slender trees, sometimes built near a tree fall. Bowers are neatly and firmly constructed with thicker, shorter, sticks in the outside bases of walls and finer longer ones within. Three in the Strickland-Nomad River areas averaged 23 centimetres long, 16 wide and 19 high externally, with the avenue 17 long and eight wide. One bower had its avenue orientation on magnetic 355°, but two others had them orientated at 30° and 55°. Decorations, up to about 10, include blue, purple and brown fruits, purple and white flowers, snail shells, or yellow-brown leaves within the avenue and blackish glossy ones outside it. Paint is applied to the inside of the avenue walls. Adult males atttend bowers at any time of year, but mostly during May to July at Nomad River and August to November near the Strickland River, Papua New Guinea. Males attend a bower during early morning and late afternoon and typically for two to four weeks, but sometimes as long as two months, before abandoning it.

Activity at one bower in the Strickland-Normad River area of Papua New Guinea on 1 September and 5 November 1987 included four visits by the adult male between 1000 to 1300 hours, these averaging almost 10 minutes in duration, with bower painting being performed on three visits. One male destroyed a bower but it was unknown if it was the owner or an intruding rival. Courtship is unrecorded but is presumably generally similar to that of the Masked Bowerbird.

Breeding

Nothing is known about nest location and situation, nest structure and building, eggs and incubation, nestling care and nestling development in the wild. The species has, however, bred a couple of times at the Al Wabra Wildlife Preservation facility in Qatar by staff of Sheikh Saoud Bin Mohammed Bin Ali Thani. Two of these breedings involved a parental incubation period of 21 and 22 days, a nestling period of 21 and 23 days, and young taking two months to start feeding independantly. An egg, nestling, and juvenile of this captive breeding are illustrated here for the first time, in Chapter 6.

Status and conservation

This is not an uncommon bird in the Wataikwa River area of southern Papua and the Fly River region of Papua New Guinea from near the coast, at Tarara, upstream to the Black River. People of the Fly River used to wear dried skins of adult males, these being traded to the coast and Daru Island. One skin was obtained at Mt Hagen, Papua New Guinea. Adult male skins were occasionally hung from vehicle rear view mirrors in the Kiunga area of Papua New Guinea in the 1990s, as status symbols. Concern has been expressed about contemporary and future forestry activity in the latter area.

A calling adult male Flame Bowerbird, captive in Qatar.

An adult male Flame Bowerbird in wing-flicking courtship display, captive in Qatar. By and courtesy of Simon B. Jensen and Al Wabra Wildlife Preservation.

ADELBERT BOWERBIRD
Sericulus bakeri

Etymology: *bakeri* after George F. Baker, Jr. (1878-1937), an east African bird collector and trustee of the American Museum of Natural History. Previously referred to as Beck's Bowerbird, after Rollo H. Beck who discovered it.

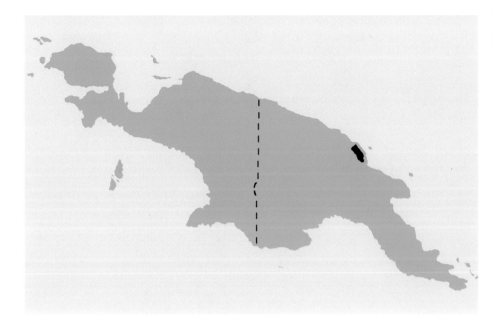

This bowerbird lives in hill forests on the Adelbert Range, Papua New Guinea, at 1200 to 1450, rarely to *c.* 900, metres above sea level.

Description

A relatively small bowerbird, less stocky than most; inconspicuous when not at bowers or perched atop bare emergent tree branches.

26 to 27 cm in length: A medium-sized silky bowerbird species: Females and immature males generally brownish-olive above, a little paler about the head, and a variable dirty whitish below washed dilute buff and finely barred or scalloped on the chin and throat and broadly barred elswhere with brownish-olive to brownish-grey. Adult males are jet black except for a rich deep flame scarlet crown and extensive filamental silky cape, arising at the lower nape, and a large patch of orange-yellow in the wings. Bill blackish, with a pale blue-grey base in adult males; eye dark brown in females and immature males, pale yellowish in adult males; legs blackish. The sexes are similar in size although adult females weigh less and have a longer tail than adult males. For pictures of this bowerbird elsewhere see page 136.

Ecology and habits

A shy, retiring, uncommon bird of mid-storey to the canopy of original hill forest and forest edge about native gardens where it visits fruiting trees. Birds often perch upon exposed, thin, bare, canopy branches. They are encountered alone, in twos or small groups of many more female-plumaged than adult male birds. Vocalisations are little known: One adult male near his bower gave a series

A rare video frame of an adult male Adelbert Bowerbird at his bower (opposite). By and courtesy of Brett Benz.

of short churrs, other notes, and mimicked the calls of the Magnificent Riflebird and Magnificent Bird of Paradise. The species also produces sharp hissing, rasping and ratchety notes.

Eats fruits, including figs and berries, and arthropods, including ants and grasshopper-like insects. Birds visit food trees in secondary growth at rainforest edges, and single birds and flocks feed in fig trees.

Bowers and courtship

Reproduces polygynously, the promiscuous males seasonally building and decorating terrestrial avenue bowers. Little is known about the traditional status of bower locations and sites. One bower was on the gentle south slope of a ridge about 60 metres below its crest in slightly disturbed primary hill forest, the broken canopy of which permitted more light to the bower than was typical of the habitat. A second bower also had no low foliage canopy above it. The small avenue is like those of other silky bowerbirds, being constructed of unbranched and curved twigs that are thicker at the outside of the bower walls. Five bowers averaged 28 centimetres long, 26 wide and 33 high externally, with the avenue 14 long and seven wide. Their avenue orientation averaged 251°. Bower decorations, up to about 50, include blue and purple fruits and, in one bower, at least one yellowish-brown leaf. Bower painting, destruction, and decoration theft remain unrecorded but all probably occur. Display months are unknown. One adult male called at his bower site and attended it during September. Courtship behaviour is unknown.

Breeding

Nest building, in the crown of a small epiphytic fern on a semi-dead tree with twiggy bare branches and several smallish epiphytes growing on it, was observed during September: The tree was on the side of a track, and stood with a tall stump and another smallish tree, isolated from the forest by a cleared area of 50 by 80 metres. The nest-building female gave a quite loud *k-zzz k-zzz* or *tk-sss tk-sss* from above her nest site, and nearby trees, where she also repeated a piping note several times. One female had an enlarged ovary in February but no other information on nesting seasonality is known. Nest building, eggs and incubation, nestling care and development remain unknown.

Status and conservation

An uncommon and vulnerable species that is moderately common locally on the small altitudinal 'island' formed by its Adelbert Mountains habitat. Birds may be sparser at the lower altitudinal range of the species but this remains to be properly demonstrated. The total range of the species has been estimated at 570 square kilometres, and its population of some 2,500 to 10,000 individuals is considered to be in continuous decline.

ADELBERT BOWERBIRD

An Adelbert Bowerbird bower, decorated with blue fruits and leaves. By and courtesy of Roy Mackay.

A rare video frame of an adult male Adelbert Bowerbird at his bower. By and courtesy of Brett Benz.

REGENT BOWERBIRD

Sericulus chrysocephalus
Etymology: *chrysocephalus* Gr. *khrusokephalos,* golden-headed (*khrusoa,* gold; - *kephalos,* headed).

Confined to the coastal zone of central eastern Australia, from immediately north of Sydney to the Connors and Clarke Ranges, Eungella Plateau, inland of Mackay, Queensland, with a distributional gap about the Fitzroy River valley inland of Rockhampton, from sea level to 900 metres, but attitudinal range varies across the species range. Known to have hybridised with the Satin Bowerbird twice.

Description

A small bowerbird, slighter and more fine-billed than others. Inconspicuous unless birds are at bowers, perched in emergent canopy trees, or flocking.

24 to 25 cm in length: A slender silky bowerbird species: Females and immature males have a variable dull dirty off-white to drab grey head finely streaked, mottled, and smudged and with a contrasting dull sooty black crown patch. The other upperparts are variably olive-brown with feathers of the mantle spotted off-white. Underparts are dirty off-white to creamish with a broad central line of dull sooty black feathers down the throat and the remainder broadly barred blackish-brown. Subadult males show some characters of both the female and the adult male plumages; Figure 1.6. Adult males are slightly glossy jet black with a brilliant yellow crown, nape, broad upper back, and an extensive patch on the wings. Bill long and fine, blackish in females and immature males, orange-yellow in adult males; eye dark brown in females and immature males, yellow in adult males; legs blackish-brown. Adult females average conspicuously larger than adult males in weight and in body size except only bill length. For pictures of this bowerbird elsewhere see pages 6, 22, 23, 39, 43, 51, 54, 58, 64, 67, 92, 100, 112, 126, 133.

Illustration of Regent Bowerbirds, adult male above and female below, from Sharpe's *Monograph ofwthe Paradiseidae and Ptilonorhynchidae* of 1891-1898 (opposite).

Ecology and habits

Birds frequent subtropical rainforest during courting and breeding, and are likely to forage as flocks into associated sclerophyll woodland and more open habitats, including cultivated country and urban gardens. In the northern part of the southeast of the species range birds altitudinally descend in winter and at times feed upon exotic orchard fruits; rates of sightings below 200 metres being 58% in autumn/winter and 22% in spring/summer. Female-plumaged birds are thought to make these winter movements three to four weeks earlier than do adult males. Regents sometimes form mixed species foraging flocks with Satin Bowerbirds and Pied Currawongs.

Adult plumaged males are shy and retiring, whereas female-plumaged birds are much bolder. Flight is strong, direct, and slightly undulating. Birds are fond of foliage bathing and they sun themselves first thing in the morning on emergent forest canopy perches. At least 14 individuals were once seen to sun bathe together, with as many as eight on the ground at any one time in typical songbird sunning postures, and some holding such postures for 10 to 15 minutes. This is one of the least vocal of bowerbirds away from bowers, and at them it vocalises only during display when softly given harsh grating and typical bowerbird notes are the most common.

Regent Bowerbirds eat fruits and animals, mostly insects, but predominantly the former. They also eat a wide variety of plants' flowers, buds, petals, nectar, seeds, and leaves. Most leaf eating occurs during the non-breeding months July to October. Of fruit eating on the Sarabah Range, southern Queensland, 67% involves drupes and berries, but some capsular fruits are also taken. Birds perch in foliage to pluck fruits, and swallow them whole when possible, but may briefly hover to snatch smaller fruits in flight. Larger fruits are torn apart *in situ*. Principal fruits in the diet change with time of year. Although Regents will forage alongside Green Catbirds, Satin Bowerbirds, and other fruit eating birds, they also actively displace them from fruiting trees. Females dominate their smaller males at feeding trees and will defend flowers from others of their kind.

Of foraging upon flowers on the Sarabah Range, 87% involved the taking of nectar. Animal foods include cicadas, earwigs, grasshoppers, beetles, and ants. In foraging for animals Regents glean from a substrate, hawk, pounce, snatch, and probe for them. Several birds, together with three species of honeyeaters, were observed to repeatedly enter an approximately 19 metre high tree trunk crevice about which numerous insects were flying and upon emerging from the crevice preened and shook themselves with no sign of water. As water was locally available, it was concluded that all of these partly nectar eating birds were raiding a native beehive for honey. Will boldly visit bird feeders.

Bowers and courtship

Regent Bowerbirds reproduce polygynously, the promiscuous males building and decorating well concealed avenue bowers. Traditional bower sites are dispersed, not clumped, through appropriate ridge top habitat. Bower sites tend to be within rainforest on flat or less sloping ground with an immediate liana-thicket cover that provides concealment and protection. The average distance between 24 bower sites over three seasons on the Sarabah Range was 195 metres. Some individual adult males live for more than 23 years. One adult male attended the same bower site for three seasons.

Unlike those of other bowerbirds, except possibly other silky bowerbirds, bowers of Regents are short-lived, mostly being maintained for 10 days or less; although occasionally for more than 25 days. When a bower is destroyed by a rival adult male, or by the owning adult male because a rival discovers it, the bower location is changed. As a result an adult male can build and attend up to four bowers in a single season. A new bower is built within the same bower site, but beneath a different liana thicket than the previous one. A new bower takes only three to fours hours to construct. One or more immature males sporadically use shorter-term rudimentary bower sites and structures.

Bowers are small, sparse, and relatively frail avenues of sticks decorated with few objects. Bower sticks often become fused together by the action of a whitish fungus. Thirty-three Sarabah Range bowers averaged 23 centimetres long and 20 wide externally, with the avenue eight wide and 18 high. Bowers are not mostly north-south orientated, presumably because they are built beneath dense vine tangles below the forest canopy, where diffused light reaches them from above and not more directly from the sides. Regents invariably decorate the central bower interior with the odd item, but only occasionally outside it. Decorations include green leaves, pale flowers and petals, seeds, fruits, snail shells, and cicada nymph ectoskeletons and can number up to about 30. Synthetic blue items may be used. Bower painting is performed, males masticating a paint of foliage and/

An immature male Regent Bowerbird, with pale bill and eye, presents his nape to an apparently 'imagined' audience during practice courtship display, Lamington, Queensland.

An adult male Regent Bowerbird courts a female, with dark bill and eye, holding a snail shell in his beak, Lamington, Queensland.

An adult male Regent Bowerbird presents his colourful nape to his pale-billed immature male audience in typical nape presentation courtship posture (opposite).

or fruit flesh to place it on the floor near the bower to repeatedly return to as they paint the inner bower walls with pecking or short jabbing strokes and bill wiping.

On the Sarabah Range males are active at bowers from September to January, but also during July and August elsewhere. Adult males spend surprising little time, about three percent of daylight, at their bower sites each day compared with other bowerbirds. Of this time all but 80% is spent in building or quietly perching, preening, bill wiping, and looking around within 20 metres of the bower; only rarely do they vocalise. On the bower males build and decorate, courtship display to a female, display to another male, display alone, or chase intruding male rivals or other birds. Males continuously destroy bowers of rivals. Damage inflicted upon a bower by its owner, because it has been discovered by a rival, is more extensive than that caused by rivals. Rebuilding of a bower by its owner may occur but not if the damage done by an intruder is severe. Adult males visiting the bower of a rival will take decorations to their own bower, and discriminate between the decorations that they will steal.

Most courtship displays, and all matings, occur only after a female arrives at a bower escorted by a bower-owning male. Bower visits by females are significantly longer at better-constructed bowers, this suggesting females are unimpressed by poorer quality ones. While males court predominantly at bowers they will also do so in trees, but such displays are less intense with limited posturing. A continuous subsong of avian mimicry is given during courtship. Initially the male stands at an entrance of his bower in an upright posture and utters a low and soft chattering and warbling while looking at the female perched above his bower. Once the female comes to his bower, he moves backward some 20 to 50 centimetres. He stands in front of the bower or perches on a nearby branch or liana, facing her, and continues to sing as she sits within the bower or an entrance. She may peck at decorations within the bower.

If the female remains the male starts his bower display, this consisting of central and peripheral elements. During central display, he remains within about 30 centimetres of a bower entrance, and stands upright facing her. Occasionally, he picks up a decoration while making sideways movements of his head and neck. He may also drop the decoration and gape, while moving his head to one side. In a slightly lowered posture, he 'wing flicks', by quickly opening and refolding one wing. Also he may then present his nape to the female by lowering his bill. Finally, he moves his head back whilst making a series of bobbing movements. During his nape presentation his plush nape feathers are erected. In a bent-forward posture, the male then raises and repeatedly flaps both wings, with bill open. During such forehead presentation, his head is bent downward and wings slightly drooped. In this posture he runs forward, his reddish forehead toward the female. This advance may be repeated, with him returning to his pre-advance location by running backwards. The above postures occur in various sequences.

During peripheral displays, he runs about within a metre of his bower.

His abrupt movements include flying, hopping, and running about the bower and immediate branches and vines. A wing being opened fully results in a flash of bright yellow. While perching briefly near his bower he performs 'wing presentations' by repeatedly opening and refolding a wing. During central displays he mostly postures facing the female, he will often be behind her during peripheral displays. The female remains crouching in the bower during both forms of display.

If a female backs out of the bower to hop to a perch, the male's song becomes slightly louder. A female's departure obviously terminates a courtship, but if she accepts the male she crouches in his avenue in a forward-tilted posture. The male then enters the avenue from behind her and mates. Copulation typically occurs within the avenue, but will occasionally occur on the court directly in front of an avenue entrance. Mated females then ruffle their plumage and vigorously shake their slightly droops wings before leaving the bower site.

Five successful courtships on Sarabah Range averaged 25 minutes in duration, while unsuccessful ones averaged only six minutes. While most courtships are uninterupted by rival males we once watched an adult male court a female to mount and copulate with her only to be flown at and knocked off the female by a subadult male who then unsuccessfully attempted to copulate with the resisting female as the adult male lay on his back.

That Regents' bowers are well hidden and their courtship vocalizations are soft suggest that birds minimise attracting attention to their visually conspicuous courtship. Where Regents live together with Satin Bowerbirds individuals of both can occur at a single bower and, extremely rarely, hybridise.

Breeding

Breeding occurs during September to February, with southerly populations starting and finishing some two weeks earlier than more northerly ones. Peak months of egg laying are November to December, with nestlings fledging from late February to early March. On average nesting lasts three to four months, but this varies with location, altitude, and weather.

The same individual female may build nests at the same location in different seasons and in the same site. Most nests are cryptically sited in dense foliage of clumps of vines, mistletoes, or other plants and typically near to the top of the plant. They average eight metres above ground, occuring from two to 31 metres high. Nests are frail shallow saucers of loosely placed sticks, with an eggcup lining of finer twigs and occasionally with a few leaves therein. They are located as close as 20 metres from an active bower. Nest building lasts about one to two weeks. Eggs are variable creamy off-whitish, with a faint hint of greenish-yellow to buff, to light and dark buff variously marked with numerous irregular brown, purple-brown to olive-brown lines and some smudging and spotting; 161 eggs average 38 x 27 millimetres. One to three eggs are laid but 84% of 128 clutches were of two eggs. In captivity eggs were laid on alternate days, the incubation period was an estimated 17 to 21 days, and the nestling period 17 days. Nestlings are fed fruit and insects, the latter including caterpillars, katydids and beetles. Advanced Sarabah Range nestlings are fed a 25% fruit diet. In captivity replacement nests are built and laid in after a nest failure, but there is no evidence of renesting after a successful one in the same season. The overall success of seven nests in the wild was 43%.

Status and conservation

The Regent was once common about Sydney but the Gosford and Hawksbury River area is now its usual southern limit. It was once far more extensive along the east coast but now occurs in fragmented and isolated pockets due to habitat loss; uncommon in small forest 'islands' but common or moderately common in larger ones. Most populations appear fairly stable today.

A young immature male Regent Bowerbird, dark-billed and in female plumage, surveys decorations on a Satin Bowerbird's bower with a view to stealing some, Lamington, Queensland.

SATIN BOWERBIRD
Ptilonorhynchus violaceus
Etymology: *Ptilonorhynchus* Gr. *ptilon*, a feather; *rhunkhos*, the bill. *Violaceus* L.
violaceous or violet-coloured.

One population occupies southeast and eastern Australia from sea level to 1100 metres, on the McPherson Range of southeast Queensland. An isolated population occurs further north, in the Wet Tropics of northeast Australia at 640 to 1220, but more typically 700 to 900, metres. Known to have hybridised with the Regent Bowerbird twice.

Description

A stocky bowerbird with feathering projecting forward over the nostrils to make the pale bill appear short. Plumages other than of adult males are unique within polygynous bowerbirds in being predominantly green. This species includes two geographical forms, or subspecies; see page 291.

28 to 33 cm in length: A medium (the northern form) to large (southern form) bowerbird. Females and immature males have a variably ashy grey-green upper body relieved by cinnamon-brown wings and upper tail. The underparts are also green with whitish striations to streaks on the chin, throat, and upper breast becoming paler lower down to fade to off-whitish scalloped and barred with greenish. Adult males are entirely highly glossy indigo blue. Bill blackish in females and immature males, pale whitish in adult males; eye blue; legs variably pale coloured. Adult females average lighter in weight than adult males and have a longer tail; tails of males become shorter as they age. For pictures of this bowerbird elsewhere see pages 5, 26, 28-29, 40, 51, 60, 68, 77, 80, 83, 96, 101, 105, 146.

Illustration of Satin Bowerbirds, adult male at left and female at right, from Sharpe's *Monograph of the Paradiseidae and Ptilonorhynchidae* of 1891-1898 (opposite).

Ecology and habits

This is a bowerbird of wet forests and woodlands, with a strong preference for rainforest edges, and adjacent tall sclerophyll woodlands with a dense sapling understory. Satins, particularly those living in woodlands, move into more open habitats during winter, when some fruit and insect foods are relative scarce, to form flocks as large as 100 to 200 birds that graze pastures. During this non-breeding period adult males travel more than a kilometre from their bower site, when males have extensively overlapping foraging ranges. Some localised movements to lower altitudes occur during winter, when social roosts occur. One adult male roosted above his bower throughout the year. Satins are fond of bathing, and they also ant and sunbathe. Adult males away from bowers are far shyer and elusive than are green plumaged birds.

Flocking birds can be vocally conspicuous, producing various harsh calls and including avian and other mimicry. The bower advertisement song of adult males is a clearly whistled *quoo - eeeew*, the brief first note ascending and the long somewhat mournful second one descending. Loud harsh churring notes are given singly or in twos or threes by males perched about bower sites. Males about bowers also give numerous other vocalizations, including sophisticated mimicry of other birds and sounds – as do females at nests.

Individuals of both sexes have lived in excess of 20 to 30 years. A Grey Goshawk once took a Satin, but predation rates at bowers are in fact extremely low. Satins eat a wide variety of fruits, as well as some flower petals, stamens and nectar, leaves, seeds, and animals, mostly insects. Woodland-dwelling birds in Beaury State Forest, New South Wales, eat more leafy matter and less fruits than rainforest-dwelling ones do. About 80% of fruit eating involves drupes and berries, but capsular fruits are also eaten. Fruits are mostly taken by birds perching upright or reaching head down to pluck fruit but some, such as large figs, are eaten *in situ* or taken in flight or from the ground. Birds not uncommonly forage in trees with Green Catbirds, Regent Bowerbirds and other fruit eating birds. When numbers of birds aggregate at a food resource aggression can be common, adult males invariably dominating younger birds. Satins are sometimes displaced by Regents from fruiting trees.

During spring and summer Satins mostly forage for plant foods in the canopy, but during winter flocks visit pastures to graze upon shoots of grasses, succulent white clover leaves, and small ground-dwelling herbaceous plants. They travel to gardens and orchards to eat cultivated green vegetables and soft fruits. Birds also eat seeds, including from bird feeders, and nectar is lapped from garden plants including grevillias, banksias, and camellias. The animal diet includes cicadas, beetles, plant bugs, stick insects, caterpillars, sawfly larvae, ants, insect eggs and preying mantis egg cases, millipedes, spiders, and winged termites taken during their nuptial flight eruptions. Most such animals are taken from foliage, but some from tree trunks, limbs, branches, twigs, and few from the ground or snatched in the air. Birds nervously visit feeders.

Bowers and courtship

Satins reproduce polygynously, the promiscuous males building and decorating an avenue bower. Traditional bower sites are uniformly dispersed throughout suitable habitat, mostly on flatter topography. Because bowers are rarely located deep within rainforest, except at tree fall sites, the dispersion of bowers within this habitat differs from that within woodland. Bower sites of adult males in each square kilometre of woodland over three seasons averaged almost five and each male could hear at least two or three rival males calling at their bowers from his own. Nearest neighbour distances between traditional bower sites in the Beaury State Forest varies between habitats: 43 woodland bowers averaged 311 metres apart, 24 rainforest edge ones 284 metres apart, and 34 bowers in a rainforested area with much regrowth and adjacent cleared and disturbed areas were 183 metres apart.

Two bower sites were in continuous use for more than 30 years and many more were in seasonally continuous occupation in excess of a decade. Individual adult males hold a bower site for an average of more than four to five seasons, but a more than 20-year-old male occupied one bower site for more than 15 years.

The death of a long established, dominant and successful, traditional bower site owning adult male is followed by fierce competition for possession of his bower site, this resulting in turn in changes to the ownership of several neighbouring bowers. Younger immature males will frequent, decorate, and display upon a particular patch of ground, usually beneath some foliage cover, with no sticks or bower structure whatever. Males of two to three years old build poorly constructed and decorated rudimentary bowers at temporary sites that are typically peripheral to traditional ones of adult males. These inferior bowers lack upright walls or have ones of unsuitable shape and sticks, compared

An immature male of the larger, southern, Satin Bowerbird visits the well-decorated bower of an adult male in his absence, Lamington, Queensland.

Males of the smaller, northern, Satin Bowerbird line the floor, and sometimes part of the walls, of their bowers with moss, Atherton Tableland, north Queensland (opposite above).

to the finer bowers of older males, and are typically not painted and are attended only sporadically by one or more immature males. The latter also often visit the bowers of adult males.

At the start of a display season each adult male builds a new bower immediately adjacent to, or actually on, the spot where the bower of the previous season stood. For example, one bower site remained that of the same adult male for 10 to 11 years, his new structures typically being built within his 25 metre diameter bower site. This repeated seasonal use of specific sites involves both individual males of the previous season(s) and males new to the area that replace previous bower owners.

The bower of an adult male typically consists of two parallel, outwardly curving, walls of sticks placed upright into a foundation platform of fine sticks and grass straws laid upon the ground. The two walls curve gently toward each

A Satin Bowerbird's bower with an additional, third, wall. Smith's Lake, New South Wales. By and courtesy of D. Schuelein.

other as they rise beyond half their length and, in some structures, form an arch as the uppermost twigs meet above the avenue floor. A male can build a bower within a day or two. Some bowers comprise of more than 2000 sticks and have up to 200 decorations, though generally less. Thirty-six Beaury State Forest bowers averaged 31 centimetres wide and 23 high externally, with their avenues 26 long and 14 centimetres wide, and the area of sticks laid upon the ground (the platform) extending beyond the avenue entrance an average of 45 centimetres. Bowers with a third wall, thus forming two adjacent avenues, do occasionally occur. These atypical bowers appear to reflect no more than the excess building activity, or drive, of a few individual males and the third wall is often only temporary. Bowers of the tropical northern population of smaller birds are smaller and typically have their avenue floor, and sometimes also one or both platforms, lined with green moss. The majority of bowers built by adult

An adult male of the smaller, northern, Satin Bowerbird courts a female in his bower, Atherton Tableland, north Queensland (opposite below).

BOWERBIRDS

males are said to have the avenue orientated along or close to a north by south axis, and those of younger males and of adult males of the smaller northern form less so, but this and is significance requires further investigation.

Conspicuously contrary to other avenue building species, male Satins do not place decorations within their avenue but only on the platforms outside its entrances. A great diversity of, mostly blue, decorations are used. Natural decorations include numerous blue, violet, purple, and greenish-yellow flowers and fruits, feathers, notably the flight feathers of Crimson Rosellas, straw coloured objects, dry leaves, greyish fungus, blue butterfly wings, beetle wing cases, preying mantis egg cases, cicada and spider ectoskeletons, brownish snail shells, sloughed snake skin pieces, mammal, bird and reptile skulls, egg shells, paper wasp nests and much more. Decorations at one bower interestingly included the lower mandible and forecrown feathers of an adult male Satin Bowerbird, and at another a dead blue-plumaged adult male Superb Fairy-wren. A vast range of man-made objects are used as decorations, including blue bags, matchboxes, cigarette packets and lighters, various paper and plastic bits, envelopes, string, marbles, glass, toys, jewellery, and even condoms!

Adult males actively paint their inner bower walls. Natural paint materials, mixed with saliva, include ground charcoal, masticated foliage, liverwort, crumbly tree bark, and fruits. Repeated painting of bower sticks results in a powdery blackish coating of one to three millimetres thick when dry. A male often drops a supply of paint at one end of the bower avenue, to then repeatedly return to his 'palate' in order to replenish his bill with paint before continuing to apply it to his walls. Males of the northern population often bring a large piece of pale, dead and dry, wood pulp to the bower and repeatedly use it as paint over several weeks. They repeatedly go to the piece of wood and audibly 'snip' tiny pieces from it and masticates them with their saliva. The result can then be seen on the birds' mandibles as a thick brown fluid that is applied to the bower walls.

The display season starts as early as May to July, with peak bower attendance being mostly August to October and declining in late November to December, but this varies between localities. While Beaury State Forest adult males spend little daylight time actually on the bower (less than 20%) they were found to spend 70% or more of the day within 50 metres of it during the peak display season, when they are more insect-eating and catch numerous beetles and cicadas. At the bower site time is spent in vocally advertising the bower site, in bower maintenance, displaying to visiting females and chasing off males. Adult males chase immature males from their bowers during the mating period but not after this. Female-plumaged immature males and rival adult males infrequently visit bowers of adult males intent upon damaging them and/or stealing decorations from them. Stealing raids are far more common than bower destruction ones. Most destruction raids are directed at the bower of the nearest rival male, and thus that of the most likely competitor for females. Bower destruction affects the quality of bowers of adjacent rival males and thus reduces the chances of them impressing and mating with females.

SATIN BOWERBIRD

Display by resident adult males to immature males occurs occasionally, but adult males display solitarily almost as often as they court females. Females approach a bower quietly and unobtrusively and are often frightened off by initially aggressive behaviour of the male. Males give mimicry in calling above bower sites and while displaying on the bower. During courtship older males produce better quality mimicry and sing longer and higher quality bouts of avian mimicry than do younger males. Females prefer older male as mates.

Two typical courtship phases are: A vocalised *buzzing* accompanied by body movements with repeatedly and rapidly opened wings, and a static phase accompanied by vocal mimicry. In the presence of a female within the bower avenue courtship follows a ritualised pattern as follows: Giving soft and high-pitched pleading squeaking and spluttering notes, the male makes his way to the entrance of his avenue she is facing. He strikes a rounded posture with folded wings held just above his back, tail down and stiffly vibrating vertically as if sprung at the base, and bill opened widely now and again. Entirely or mostly hidden from her by the end of a bower wall, he faces the bower and repeatedly picks at or picks up a decoration. At first he vigorously shakes his head after dropping the decoration, as if in distaste, and may also mouth gape at the female. With a decoration in his beak his head and bill are jerked vertically up and down or shaken vigorously. His body is now held at about 45 degrees to the ground, bill down and tail up, and raised high on exposed thighs as his soft pleading calls

An adult male of the larger, southern, Satin Bowerbird in a courtship display posture alone at his bower, Lamington, Queensland.

continue. Suddenly his vocalizations change to a continuous mechanical-like whirring *buzz*. His tail feathers are slightly fanned and parted from one another in the vertical plane to form an inverted V shape. He then raises his tail to above 45 degrees and performs a series of 12 or more extremely vigorous upward flicks of the closed, but sometimes half open, wing farthest from his bower. Often the first of these wing flicks involves both wings. Each wing flick is punctuated by a louder whirring *buzz* call.

He then strides across his bower entrance, and thus into full view of the female, while giving one, two, or three extremely vigorous fully opened wing, sometimes both wings, flicks accompanied by a louder *buzz* call. During this movement, before, between, and after the wing flick(s), his body is held in a ritualised rounded upright posture, or sometimes a sleeked horizontal one, usually with a decoration held in the beak and his tail horizontal to the ground or lower. Stiffly bouncing movements of his tail give the impression it is attached by a spring. This striding phase takes him to the opposite position on his bower court. Here he is once again concealed from the female, by the other bower wall, and again faces her position and picks at or picks up a decoration while giving more wing flicks. He then repeats his striding display across the bower entrance, thus returning to where he started his courtship.

The male again faces his bower entrance and is again mostly or entirely hidden from the female save perhaps for his bill or head. He lowers his head to pick at or hold a decoration while holding his tail high above his back, and then may give an occasional double wing flick, but this time by flicking them out to his sides. During this phase he performs a *rattle* followed by a continuous *Vocal display* of avian mimicry mixed with odd ticking or tapping notes, and he repeatedly lifts his head and beak to look in the female's direction with a decoration in his beak. At this point a sleeked bowing posture with raised tail and/or a posture with ruffled plumage and arched back and drooped wings and tail may be performed. He may also turn his lowered beak away to present his nape to the female while holding a decoration, or hide behind a bower wall. In this stationary, mimicry-producing, phase he repeatedly raises and lowers himself slightly by flexing his legs. He often interrupts these static postures by strutting back and forth, in circular movements, across his court. If the female solicits, by crouching and vibrating her lowered wings and raising her rump, the male quickly strides past the avenue entrance and down the outside length of his bower to enter the far entrance and mate the female, often with a decoration still in his beak.

In courting, a male will pick up and use as a prop relatively dull and inconspicuous decorations rather than blue ones, but sometimes brighter yellow leaves. Leaves are more commonly held by courting males than are other decorations. Two adult males courted with a live cicada held in their beak, which were quickly eaten by the female when dropped by the male. Mating typically takes place within the bower, occasionally on the platform immediately adjacent to it, and sometimes elsewhere within a few metres of the bower. Females

A courtship display posture of an adult male of the smaller, northern, Satin Bowerbird, Atherton Tableland, north Queensland.

vigorously flutter their wings immediately following mating. One female that had been courted by a male as she stood in his bower for some 45 minutes was then attacked by him before hopping onto an adjacent perch and laying an egg before flying off! The same adult male mated one female at the same bower over two consecutive seasons, but other females may chose the same or a different male each year.

Breeding

Nesting occurs from late August or during September through to January, with egg laying peaking during November to December. Nestlings leave the nest until late February. On average nesting lasts three and a half months each year, but this varies with location, altitude, weather, and food availability. Nesting locations, even specific nest sites, can be repeatedly used by the same individual female: One female exhibited fidelity to the same nesting location over three successive seasons. Five simultaneously active Beaury State Forest woodland nests averaged 285 metres apart, and five simultaneously active rainforest nests 133 metres apart. The distance nests average to the nearest active traditional bower site also varies between habitats: in woodland 11 active nests averaged 313 metres, in rainforest 14 nests averaged 122 metres, and in a rainforested area with much regrowth, and adjacent cleared and disturbed areas 53 nests averaged 85 metres from the nearest active bower. Females predominatly forage within 100 metres of their nests (85% of 255 sightings). Female home breeding range encompasses an average of some five bower sites, and a female might visit those of at least three males. In the Bunya Mountains, southern Queensland, female Satins had an average home range of about 13-14 hectares in typical years, but in particularly dry seasons this area is roughly doubled.

Nests are built mostly in trees and bushes, but also in vine tangles about trees, in mistletoe clumps, 'suckering' tops of broken-off tree trunks and, rarely, in tree fern crowns or tree stump cavities. Nest height above ground averages 15 metres, but ranges from two to 40 metres; variation in nest site and height differs between habitats. Nests consists of a shallow saucer of sticks and twigs, broken off trees, with an eggcup lining of both green and dry leaves. Nests take one to two weeks to build. Mating takes place before or after nest building and over a month prior to egg laying.

Eggs are pale to dark buff in ground colour variably and heavily blotched and spotted with blacks, browns, greys and purple-greys, a few may also be marked with the kind of vermiculations that are more typical of the other avenue bower builders; 150 eggs average 43 x 30 millimetres. One to three eggs are laid but most clutches (66% of 98) are of two. Eggs are laid on alternate days. Two eggs in two nests hatched a day apart. The incubation period is 21 to 22 days and the nestling period 17 to 21 days. The proportion of time that females spend brooding nestlings decreases with increasing nestling age but does continue until nestlings depart the nest. Overall feeding rate is greater for broods of two than for broods of one nestling. The nestling diet is initially of invertebrates only, the overall nestling diet involving little fruit, and up to 95% insects. Principle foods include scarab beetles, cicadas, grasshoppers and other orthopterans, and stick insects. Fledglings are also fed insect and fruits. A female continued to feed her two offspring 59 days after they left the nest.

Females allocate an extraordinary amount of time to anti-predator behaviour. A female will aggressively chase away others of her kind as well as other potential predators of her eggs or nestlings. These include Australian Magpies, Pied Currawongs and other species that land within or close to her nest tree as she is nest building, incubating, brooding, or feeding young. Nesting females do not attack raptors or kookaburras. Instead, if a potential predator such as a Brown Goshawk perches near her nest, she refrains from visiting it and adopts a 'frozen' posture. In one such instance a female 'froze' in a tree for 48 minutes before a goshawk, perched in the same tree, flew away; she then waited another six minutes before flying to her nest tree, paused there for another 26 minutes, and then fed her young. Females will mimic the calls of potential predators, such as kookaburras, goshawks, magpies and humans, as their nests are approached by a potential predator of nest contents. In the presence of a person females with young may also perform a 'broken wing' distraction display while mimicking the calls of potential predators.

The overall success of five Beaury State Forest nests was 25%, each female producing an average of a fraction more than one third of a fledged young each season. Replacement clutches are produced after the loss of the first, but true second broods within a season are exceptional: The only such evidence from the wild is for an individually identifiable female successfully raising two broods in a season when insect food was conspicuously abundant. At Taronga Park Zoo, Sydney, a captive female laid a single egg clutch 41 days after the fledging of her first brood of that season. Many different mammals, birds, and reptiles will predate eggs and nestlings.

Status and conservation

The Satin Bowerbird remains a common to reasonably abundant bird in remaining habitat, but has lost a good deal to human land use that has fragmented its distribution. It has decreased at Nanango, southeast Queensland since the 1950s. Population increases in the suburban gardens and parks of Canberra, Australian Capital Territory, developed since the mid 1970s, are well documented. Satins were once subjected to significant hunting by people otherwise shooting pigeons visiting fruiting forest trees.

LAUTERBACH'S BOWERBIRD

Chlamydera lauterbachi
Etymology: *lauterbachi* after German botanist Carl Lauterbach (1864-1937),
who discovered it in 1896.

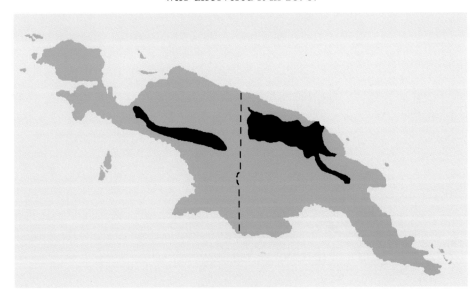

Occupies mainland New Guinea from lowlands to about 1800 metres above sea level. Patchily in grasslands of Weyland, Snow, and Star Mountains of Papua and central and east Highlands of Papua New Guinea, east to upper Ramu River: One record for Bewani at the base of the north Coastal Range. Occurs locally together with the Fawn-breasted Bowerbird in some areas, but hybrids between the two are unknown.

Description

A relatively slender and most timid bowerbird of New Guinea that typically occurs singly or in small parties. This species includes two similar geographical forms, or subspecies; see page 291.

27 cm. A small and slight species of grey bowerbird with brownish-olive upperparts and pale buff-yellow to olive feather edging and larger spotting to the ends of flight feathers. In the Ramu River area the crown has a coppery-rose glossy sheen but elsewhere birds have an olive sheen. Chin to upper breast greyish to pale yellow with dark dusky grey-brown feather edges producing strong streaking, and the remainder of underparts sandy yellow with indistinct pale brown barring on sides of breast and down onto the flanks. Bill black, eye dark brown; legs brownish to greyish. The sexes are alike; adult males are heavier, and have a slightly longer wing, than females. For pictures of this bowerbird elsewhere see pages 77, 96, 107.

Ecology and habits

Lauterbach's inhabits lowland and mid-montane secondary growth, remnant forest patches and forest edges, overgrown gardens and associated or adjacent bushy grasslands, pit-pit grass, cane grass swamps, coffee plantations, and stands of *Casuarina*. It is extremely nervous and wary in approaching exposed trees, alone or in small groups, but can be curious. Birds like to perch on high exposed perches and are extremely timid at bowers.

Calls include a sharp *chilp chilp chilp* and rasping, grating, churring, rattling and hissing calls typical of other grey bowerbirds. An alarm vocalisation

Illustration of Lauterbach's Bowerbirds from the German ornithological journal *Journal für Ornithologie* for 1897 (opposite).

257

is described as sounding like a "rap on a cardboard box". Birds mimic environmental sounds and while mimicry of other birds in the wild is likely this awaits confirmation. Captive birds mimic numerous audible native bird calls and unbird-like mechanical sounds including grating notes and sharp clicks and what sounded like footsteps upon gravel, water flowing quickly over gravel, chainsaws, hammering, and pig squealing. Diet is little known but includes fruits and insects, including caterpillars and beetles.

Bowers and courtship

Reproduces polygynously, the promiscuous males building and decorating elaborated avenue bowers. Traditional bower sites are amid dense vegetation in partially shaded situations under large bushy trees, just inside the edge of extensive forest or forest patches adjacent to kunai or pit-pit grassland with dispersed shrubs and trees. Sixteen bower sites at Kup, Wahgi River, Papua New Guinea, were within an area of about ten square kilometres. In suitable habitat bowers can be half to one kilometre apart and be traditionally used for more than 10 years. Bowers are often on level ground, sometimes atop dry hillsides or small rises, beneath bushes, but sometimes in marshy areas the substantial stick base will serve as an island. The avenue bower is unique in having four walls built upon a substantial stick and grass cane base, and in having the walls of the main avenue angled outward rather than vertical or arched over the avenue. At each end of the main avenue the platforms are extensively developed and elaborated into additional walls that form cross-passages at right angles to the central avenue. The inner two walls are the shortest and are lined with fine grass stems.

Four bowers in the Baiyer River Valley, Papua New Guinea, averaged 64 centimetres long, 67 wide and 43 high, with the main avenue averaging 23 long and 10 wide. The exposed platforms of sticks at either end of the avenue averaged 84 long and 17 centimetres deep. No favoured orientation of the central avenue is apparent. More than 1000 decorations can be on a bower. Together with their decorations, bowers weighed 3-7.5 kilograms; the heaviest having nearly 1000 stones of almost 4.5 kilograms. A bower can consist of more than 3000 sticks, lined with more than 1000 strands of brownish grass.

Bower decorations are predominantly grey to blue-grey river-washed pebbles and large spherical blue quandong fruits, but medium to small red, blue-grey, and brown fruits, and blue-grey seeds are also used. Pebbles and larger blue fruits are placed against and into the sticks of the inner end walls and in the centre of the avenue but red decorations are on the bower floor between the avenue entrance and the end walls or on the ground outside and beside the bower. In areas where stones are rare much charcoal is used. Bower painting is frequent, involves much time, and is extensive in area to leave conspicuous staining.

The display season is mainly April to January. Males spend a great deal of time at bowers during the courting season; adult males we watched at two different Baiyer River bower sites averaged 21% of daylight present, where

An adult male Lauterbach's Bowerbird standing between his central bower avenue, to his right, and one of his end walls, to his left, Baiyer River, Papua New Guinea (opposite).

they will chase off intruding males. Males attack bowers of rivals during their absence: entering the central avenue to vigorously tear out inner sticks by their bases. Decoration theft is unrecorded but doubtless occurs.

During 52 hours of observation by us a male bower owner directed numerous, relatively simplistic, displays at a female standing or crouching within his central avenue. These included two successful courtships, three days apart. An arriving female promptly enters the central avenue to remain still, save occasionally turning her head and touching or picking at the sticks of the walls. The male then hops on the spot beside a central avenue wall and approaches the avenue entrance the female faces, while giving soft grating or churring notes followed by low plaintive ones, and presents his unadorned nape to the female by turning his beak away from her often while repeatedly picking up a decoration and jerking his head up and down. He infrequently intersperses this nape presentation by turning to face the female to present a decoration while flicking his tongue in and out with simultaneous soft vocalizations. If not holding a decoration his mouth is gaped widely to expose its orange interior, as his tongue is flicked in and out, often accompanied by sharp jerking head movements. Toward the end of his nape presentation he intensifies it by twisting his head and neck even further away from the female and toward his tail, which

he fans and pulls around toward his beak, while occasionally jerking his body to flick his wing on the bill-to-tail side of his body. At any point in courting, but more often at this one, he adopts an upright posture and sharply flick one or both wings upward accompanied by loud hissing, as his bill is widely opened at the female. Red fruits can feature conspicuously in courtship, the male holding one in his beak while displaying.

Presumably in response to a female soliciting, a male suddenly stops displaying and runs quickly into the far end of his bower to mount and mate the female from behind. While mating he flaps his open wings and then flies to perch close by as the female vigorously flutters her wings and leaves the bower site. Courtship lasts but a few minutes to more than half an hour prior to mating. A male may postpone courtship to chase other males from his bower site. During such evictions a female remains in the bower until the male returns and, thus, can remain within a bower for as long as 50 minutes prior to mating.

Breeding

Breeding is known for all months except May. Eggs found in nests in April

An adult male Lauterbach's Bowerbird in nape presentation posture, at right, directed at a female in his bower avenue and who's tail is visible at left, Baiyer River, Papua New Guinea.

and during June to January. Most nests are in trees, bushes and saplings, but sometimes in grasses. Nests average two, but range from one to four, metres above ground. Habitual nest site use is unrecorded. Four Baiyer River nests ranged from 50-366, averaged 204, metres from the nearest active bower. Nests are neat compact shallow cups of fine twigs, vine tendrils, dried grasses, and the odd thin strand of bark placed upon a sparse, unkempt, foundation of dry sticks. Eggs are pale pearl grey and heavily marked throughout, more so around the larger end, with grey, blackish, and black vermiculations. Only single-egg clutches; 14 eggs average 38 x 27 millimetres. Little is known of nestling care save that we observed young fed insects. Incubation and nestling periods, nestling development, and productivity are unknown.

Status and conservation

Can be locally fairly common and conspicuous and yet elsewhere scarce. Common to abundant in the mid-mountain Wahgi and Baiyer Valleys, and in savanna and woodland of the drier Ramu Valley, but uncommon on the Sepik River.

An adult male Lauterbach's Bowerbird mates with a female within the central avenue on his bower, Baiyer River, Papua New Guinea.

FAWN-BREASTED BOWERBIRD

Chlamydera cerviniventris
Etymology: *cerviniventris* Mod. L. *cervinus*, yellowish-brown; *ventris*, the belly.

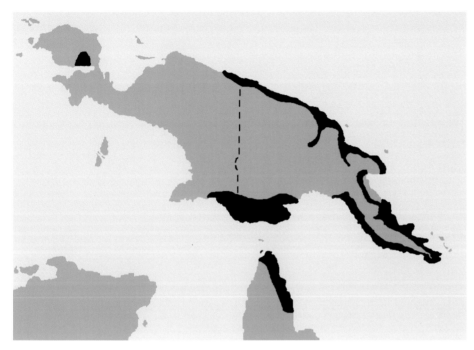

This bowerbird mostly occupies coastal areas of east New Guinea, at sea level to 500, rarely 1500 or more, metres, to at least Humboldt Bay in the north and the Kurik area of the Trans-Fly in the south, of Papua New Guinea. Populations are isolated in the Ransiki and Kebor Valleys on the east Vogelkop of Papua. Birds live in the Jimi Valley of Papua New Guinea at 1700 metres and some 145 kilometres inland, and also in the Aiyura Valley at the same altitude. Occurs together with Lauterbach's Bowerbird in some local areas, and in some local areas on Australia's Cape York Peninsula it lives among Great Bowerbirds, but hybrids involving it are unknown.

Description

Less stocky, slightly more slender, than all bowerbirds except Lauterbach's, the Golden and silky bowerbirds. No geographical variation, notwithstanding its isolated populations.

29 cm in length: A medium-sized grey bowerbird, greyer and more glaucous than Lauterbach's, with brownish-olive upperparts and paler striations and streaking about the face and head and whitish edging and spotting to the tips of the back and flight feathers. Chin, throat, and chest pale buff with broad dusky grey-brown feather edging giving a streaked appearance, and the remainder of underparts a clean pale warm cinammon. Bill blackish, eye dark brown; legs greyish-brown to blackish. The sexes are alike; while adult males are heavier than adult females they are similar in size. Birds of New Guinea and Australia are similar in size. For pictures of this bowerbird elsewhere see pages 1, 9, 77, 79.

Ecology and habits

In New Guinea Fawn-breasted Bowerbirds inhabit lowland to hill forest patches and *Eucalyptus-Melaleuca* woodland in savanna and other light woodland and scrub in extensive savanna and grassland, or forest and mangrove edges abutting it. They also occupy larger grassy areas within forest. Birds are common in parks, gardens, and teak plantations of the Port Moresby area. On Cape York

Illustration of Fawn-breasted Bowerbirds from Gould's *The Birds of Australia* Supplement of 1869 (opposite).

Peninsula birds occupy mangroves and *Melaleuca* bordering them, as well as open and closed forest where they meet Great Bowerbirds.

Birds are normally shy and wary, but are at times noisy and conspicuous. Individuals are usually alone or in twos, but sometimes in loose small groups of 10 or so, particularly in winter, foraging in trees and shrubs. They are fond of perching on exposed higher branches of trees, and their flight over larger distances is purposeful and slightly undulating. Birds visit water to drink and bathe, particularly in dry weather.

Calls include numerous and varied harsh churring, sputtering, rattling, and other typically grey bowerbird notes, with repeated loud, harsh, drawn-out rasping or hissing notes and slurred hollow whistles dominating. Many vocalizations have a ventriloqual quality, including much vocal avian and other mimicry, and a male vocalizing at his bower frequently sounds like more than one bird calling simultaneously. Sounds produced by a hand-held male included vocal mimicry of bird calls including scrubfowl, parrots, goshawks, orioles, and friarbirds, mimicry of the sounds of a whinnying and walking horse, running water, metallic-like sounds and a human voice saying 'hello, good morning…' and more. Little is known other than that the diet includes fruits and insects.

Bowers and courtship

Reproduces polygynously, the promiscuous males building and decorating a substantially based avenue bower. Traditional bower sites are in shade of low bushes in open savannah or woodland, just inside the edge of gallery forest or mangroves, or within tall secondary growth. Bowers average roughly 500 metres apart. As in other bowerbirds, younger males build, decorate and attend bowers of older males during their absence, or build rudimentary bowers between established traditional sites of older males.

Adult male Fawn-breasted Bowerbirds decorate their bower platforms and walls with green fruits, Iron Range, Queensland.

The bower avenue is built atop a substantially deep base of sticks a metre or so long that extends beyond each avenue entrance to form elevated platforms, one invariably larger and better formed than the other. At any locality bowers vary in size and dimensions. The base of two bowers in the Jimi Valley, Papua New Guinea, averaged 98 centimetres long, 66 wide, and 14 thick. Their bower avenues averaged 30 long and 28 high externally with the central avenue eight centimetres wide. A particularly large Port Moresby bower was 168 centimetres long, 81 wide, and 61 tall, including a base platform height of 41 centimetres. Bowers on Cape York Peninsula differ little in size from those of New Guinea. The compass orientation of the bower avenue is variable.

Bower decorations, numbering up to 100 or more, include small bunches of green spherical or ovate fruits, seed pods, flower buds, and green leaves. Some bowers have the addition of numerous fine rootlets placed horizontally along the sticks at the top of the walls. Paint is applied to the inner bower walls by males pushing their beak tip gently and repeatedly between the sticks.

Adult males maintain bowers for about eight to nine months of each year. The display season is mainly June to December, but varies between localities. A new bower is built every season within the same bower site, often in the same undergrowth, usually three to four metres from the last structure but almost invariably within a 15 metres radius of it. At the end of a season parts of avenue walls may be pulled down but it is not known if this is performed by the owner or by rivals.

Courtship is not well known, but it is in part similar to Lauterbach's Bowerbird, with the addition of more expansive movements about the bower more typical of other grey bowerbirds. In the presence of a female, a male performs a 'peripheral' display by crouching low and moving quickly and jerkily about his bower, up to 10 metres away, zigzagging in and out of ground cover. The bower remains his focal point, frequently returning to it and occasionally passing through its avenue. At times he stops still on the bower, head down and churring, with a bower wall between him and the avenue. Upon a female entering the avenue he postures at the end of it the female faces. Throughout display he twists his head to one side, in nape presentation. He jerks his head and neck and/or parts of his body and pulls his fanned tail toward his turned head and bill. His wings remain folded; the tail, sometimes held normally and sometimes open or closed, is often dropped to the ground or occasionally elevated to come forward until almost directly over his head. In nape presentation to a female within his avenue he may alternately crouch low onto his bower platform and stand up stiffly erect by a violent jumping, accompanied by a rhythmically pumping, sputtered, vocalization. His beak mostly remains open, accompanied by low churring noises. He will at times pick up a bunch of green fruits, holding it in his beak with head twisted to one side, while displaying.

A successful courtship consists of a female entering the avenue to be followed by the male taking up position on the platform at the entrance the female faces. He adopts the nape presentation pose, during which he infrequently swings and then holds his tail toward the side of his lowered head. If not holding a decoration he occasionally opens his mouth but does not gape widely or shake his head or tongue. He utters soft harsh vocalizations and mimicry. No additional courtship precedes him rushing to the far end of his avenue to mount and mate the female from behind. After mating he returns to his original display position to again direct nape presentation at the female who vigorously shakes her wings and flies away.

We saw one female remain motionless in a bower during a male's eight minute absence. Upon his return he ran directly at the bower from 15 metres away with sleeked plumage, giving metallic hiss-churrings. He then gave a nape presentation display and alternately presented a fruit and a twig to her as calling and exposing his mouth and tongue. Then he mated with the female who afterward perched near the bower to vigorously flutter her wings before re-entering the bower to be mounted again, after which she hopped onto the main platform and wing-fluttered before leaving.

Breeding

Breeding occurs in all months across New Guinea but peak months of egg laying vary between localities. On Cape York Peninsula birds nest from September to December, with peak laying in November. A fledged juvenile was seen accompanying a female in January. Nests are mostly built in large trees, bushes, and shrubs, but also in mangroves, from half to ten metres above ground; and

An adult male Fawn-breasted Bowerbird arrives on his bower platform with building material, Portland Roads, north Queensland.

can be habitually built at the same site over years. Six nests averaged 143 metres from the nearest active bower.

Nests have a fairly large foundation of sticks, vine tendrils, sometimes with strips of bark, and are lined with finer twiglets, a few curly vine tendrils, and/or sometimes dry grass stems. Eggs are creamy with faint hint of greenish or buff colour heavily marked with long vermiculations of browns and black, more so about their larger end. Only single egg clutches known; 24 eggs average 41 x 28 millimetres. The incubation period is unknown, but one nestling remained in the nest for 21 days before fledging.

We watched a nestling at Jimi Valley being fed insects, including caterpillars and beetles, and fruit. A female defended her nestling by flying to a nearby tree and giving a harsh *churr*, to then hop to the ground and move slowly and feebly away with drooped and fluttering wings while mimicking calls of potential predators. Nothing else of significance is known about nestling care or development.

Status and conservation

Patchily common in places but otherwise scarce to absent. Said to be common in south New Guinea but local and less so in the north. It is possible that some upland Papua New Guinea localities have been colonised by birds subsequent to their habitat modification by agriculture. A 10 hectare area of coastal hill savanna near Port Moresby contained an average of 1.3 birds and one active bower over 12 months.

An adult male Fawn-breasted Bowerbird directs a nape presentation courtship display posture at a female within his avenue bower, Iron Range, Queensland.

SPOTTED BOWERBIRD
Chlamydera maculata
Etymology: *Chlamydera* Gr. *khlamus* a short cloak; *dere,* [on] the neck. *maculata*
spotted or blotched.

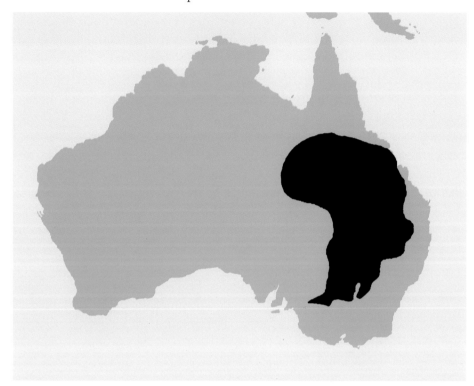

This species lives in the interior of Queensland, south of 20 degrees south, except the extreme west and southwest: Also in the extreme west and in central New South Wales except the extreme west border country, and a small distribution into the extreme northwest corner of Victoria and just into South Australia on the Murray River system. Birds occur from sea level to 500 metres or more. Vagrants appear in odd places. Spotteds co-exist with Great Bowerbirds about 100 kilometres south-southeast of Charters Towers, Queensland, where their favoured habitats abut and hybridisation between them occurs rarely.

Description

A compact, vocal, and animated bowerbird of drier Australia, cryptically plumaged in its open woodland habitats.

29 cm in length: A medium-sized grey bowerbird with a variable warm buff head striated and streaked with warm greyish and the nape decorated with an erectile filamentous pink nape crest. Upperparts variably blackish-brown conspicuously and grossly spotted with large paler, amber or clay-coloured, tips to the mantle, back, and flight feathers. Underparts pale buff to cream-coloured scalloped and barred with drab greyish, and a dilute pale yellowish wash over the lower belly and undertail area. Bill blackish, eye dark brown; legs olive-brown. The sexes are alike, but females may have no crest or a smaller one than adult males. Adult males and females are similar in size. For pictures of this bowerbird elsewhere see pages 41, 42, 59, 61, 64, 66, 84, 89, 108, 134.

Ecology and habits

This is a bird of brigalow and eucalypt woodlands, with a preference for riverine woodland. Birds commonly associate with homesteads in the interior, where males build bowers in the shade of exotic plants and are welcomed by some

Illustration of Spotted Bowerbirds, adult male in foreground and female behind, from Sharpe's *Monograph of the Paradiseidae and Ptilonorhynchidae* of 1891-1898 (opposite).

people as novel companions. Conversely, their taste for soft fruits and green vegetables, grown about homesteads, leads to the illegal destruction of numerous birds by less tolerant people. In excess of 50, but more usually 10 to 30, birds form flocks when not attending bowers or nests. Flight is swift and direct, by a series of undulations, typical of grey bowerbirds: At the apex of each undulation the wings are briefly closed, to be reopened with each dip in flight; primary tips are well separated and curl upward at the end of down beats. In flying above vegetation birds keep close to the canopy.

Vocal repertoire is diverse, consisting mostly of loud and harsh churrings and other notes, typical of the grey bowerbirds. Mimicry of other bird calls and human-made sounds is common. Cat meowing, dog barking, the noise of cattle breaking through scrub, mammals walking through fallen dead branches or crashing through twanging fence-wires, wood-chopping, the crack of a stockwhip, and whirring-like noises made by flying Crested Pigeons are some sounds mimicked. Foraging birds also mimic calls of these and other birds, including Noisy Miners, even outside display or breeding seasons. Males at bowers in the presence of people or other potential predators include the calls of several predatory birds, such as whistling kites, kookaburras, butcherbirds and magpies, as well as those of other bird species. Females at their nests do likewise in the presence of a potential predator. Raptors, including goshawks, predate Spotted Bowerbirds at bowers. A Brown Falcon killed one away from a bower. Some individuals live in excess of 13 years.

The diet is primarily of fruits, flowers, and seeds, but animals eaten include grasshoppers, beetles, ants, and spiders. Birds boldly visit gardens and bird feeders.

Bowers and courtship

Reproduces polygynously, the promiscuous males building and decorating grassy avenue bowers. Traditional bower sites are dispersed throughout open eucalypt woodland and brigalow. Bower sites average one to two kilometres apart, but can be less than a kilometre apart beneath suitable bushes when available. Preferred sites are those with larger thorny bushes, that are darker shaded, producing fruits that are eaten. Traditional ones commonly persist for at least 10 to 20 years. Some individual adult males occupied particular traditional bower sites for at least six years. As in other bowerbirds, younger males attend the bowers of older males in their absence in order to build and decorate, or build rudimentary bowers between the established traditional sites of their elders. Groups of up to 16 immature males may frequent a bower to build and display at it. Rival males damage one anothers' bowers. Relatively better bower quality and reproductive success are thought to reflect greater individual male age.

Bowers are rebuilt each season under the same bush, upon the exact same spot or immediately nearby, or under an adjacent bush. Two bowers we studied were each built at the same site for more than 16 consecutive years. At one locality the remains of eight former bowers were within 50 metres of the active one. Sites of former bowers are sometimes indicated by accumulations of pebbles or bones remaining long after the bower structures have disappeared.

Bowers are large and relatively wide avenues. Twelve Bullamon Plains, Queensland, bowers averaged 48 centimetres wide and 34 high externally, and the avenue 59 long and 20 wide. The 'mat' extension beyond the avenue averaged 118 centimetres. Typically the outside basal walls are of sticks and the remainder of grass stems. One rudimentary bower consisted of two sparse and meagre walls of fine sticks and several grass stems decorated only with three grey-green leaves and another was but an extensive area of fine twigs and grass stems laid upon the ground beside an equally extensive area of bare ground. Several presumably immature male birds attempted, but failed, to stand sticks upright into this mat of sticks. Bower avenues are predominantly orientated east-west, but there is much varation across the range of the species.

In an area where this bird lives together with the Great Bowerbird, each visiting and adding material to bowers of the other, the closest a bower of one species was to that of the other was 1200 metres. Preferences for certain items as bower decorations varies geographically but they include snail shells, bleached bones, water-worn pebbles, emu egg shell fragments, green berries, leaves, seeds and seed pods, red stems, yellow flowers, arthropod exoskeletons and grub cases, brown, clear, and green glass, black plastic, wire, foil, aluminium can pull tags and other metal, and white plastic milk container ring seals etc. A lone male that built a bower beyond his own species range, but within that of the Satin Bowerbird, decorated it for several years with blue items as Satin Bowerbirds typically do but Spotted Bowerbirds do not.

Due to its familiarity with people this bird take numerous items from homes, camps, and vehicles for bower decoration. Tales of males stealing items abound, involving all kinds of jewellery, particularly rings, shiny tools and even a bushman's glass eye. Car keys have been removed from vehicles, to be recovered from the nearest active bower by those aware of this bowerbird's behaviour. Males paint the grass stems forming the interior of their bowers walls, paint consisting of masticated grass mixed with saliva. This is applied with short strokes of the beak, mostly wiping the stems with the side of the beak but sometimes by passing them between the mandibles.

The display season extends from April to January, peak months being July-November, but with some geographic variation. Adult males spend more than 50% of daylight present at their bower site. During this time they perch at about five metres or lower near their bower, within a 100 metre radius of it, and call from regularly frequented perches at about five to 10 minute intervals. The rest of the time they spend on the ground, usually in silence, in bower maintenance, displaying alone or displaying to and chasing other Spotted Bowerbirds. The latter include both visiting females and intruding rival adult males intent upon bower damage or decoration theft. Rival males will fly into bowers to interrupt courtship and try to copulate with females being courted. Bower owning males chase Grey-crowned Babblers, Apostlebirds, Brown Snakes, lizards and other

animals away from their bowers.

Courtship display is central and/or peripheral: The former involves the male standing among bower decorations on the court immediately adjacent to the bower and the latter involves the male posturing while running around the bower in wide circles. Peripheral displays more often follow central ones, with both involving the male more or less expanding his lilac crest. Four conspicuous central display postures are described as: *Upright, Raised-wings, Sideways crest-presentation* and *Forward crest-presentation.* These might appear in any order and be accompanied by various vocalizations. The display movements are erratically jerky and violent, with the male frequently leaping upward to its own height to usually alight some 15 centimetres farther from the bower than he took off from. The male repeatedly darts rapidly forward toward the female in his avenue and back again, often picking up decorations and aggressively shaking them from his beak. Males in the Charters Towers area sometimes perform a *Nape presentation* display like other avenue building bowerbirds.

In peripheral display males raise the head, stiffen the neck, and open the beak. The tail is cocked up and wings drooped loosely, much like Great Bowerbirds. In doing this males do not hop but walk or run with their crest erect, whilst hissing as circling the bower. Copulation takes place in or immediately adjacent to the avenue. Courtship lasts from minutes to more than an hour. Only six of a population of 12 males studied near Bullamon Plains performed a total of 15 copulations, one male performing six, one four, one two, and three only one of these during observations over three months. Mating involved two to four seconds and females shook their bodies, with violently fluttering wings, immediately afterward. Females near Bullamon Plains stand perpendicular to the orientation of the length of the bower avenue, in order to watch the male direct his courtship at the broad side of an outer bower wall, but this is not the case at Taunton National Park, Queensland.

During the animated running of the peripheral display the male raises and lowers his head as simultaneously moving his body with jerky and undulating actions, reminiscent of swimming, as his folded wings are drooped and then raised while the tail remains low. The crest of the courting male is erected in a fan shape, as in Western Bowerbirds but not in the circular shape of displaying Great Bowerbirds. Bower decorations are held in the male's beak during some two percent of courtship time. Decorations are repeatedly picked up and violently thrown down. Occasional the displaying bird leaps upward and/or backward, sometimes simultaneously flicking his wings, to resume the swimming-like running motion. In moving away from their bowers males are less vocal than in moving toward them, and use two distinctive postures: a *rooster* pose, in which their head and tail are held high, wings horizontally away from the body, and the legs moved in a prancing gait; and a *penguin* pose, in which the body is erect with neck extended and head held high, tail down, and wings tight against the body, as they move with small rapid steps with the legs kept close together.

A unique photograph of an adult male Spotted Bowerbird, in foreground, watching an adult male Great Bowerbird displaying to a hybrid individual, resulting from the crossing of a Spotted with a Great Bowerbird, in his bower avenue, Charters Towers. Queensland (opposite).

An adult male Spotted
Bowerbird displays to a female
within his grass avenue bower,
Charters Towers, Queensland.

A courting adult male Spotted
Bowerbird hides from a female,
standing within his bower
avenue, behind a bower wall,
Charters Towers, Queensland.

An adult male Spotted
Bowerbird practices his nape
presentation courtship posture.
Charters Towers, Queensland.

Breeding

Over the species range as a whole the breeding season is prolonged, being July to March, with October to February the peak months for egg laying. Nests are built mostly in trees and bushes but occasionally in mistletoe clumps, saplings, and vine tangles at three to 12, and an average of six, metres above ground. Habitual use of a nest site or tree over consecutive years is not unusual. Forty-seven nests at various localities averaged 400 metres from the closest active bower.

The nest consists of a bulky, loose, foundation of dead twigs and sticks and an eggcup of fine twiglets, sometimes with dried grass stalks. Eggs are pale green-grey but variable to buffish, rarely almost creamy-buff, heavily marked with long vermiculations of browns and black; 219 eggs average 39 x 26 millimetres. One to three eggs are laid but 88% of 131 clutches were of two eggs. The difference in size between two nestlings of a brood suggests that eggs are laid on alternate days. Two eggs in one nest hatched a day apart. At one nest we studied brooding ceased when nestlings were 14 to 15 days old. The incubation period is unknown, but in one nest the nestling period was 21 days.

Fruits and insects are fed to nestlings. Animal foods consist mostly of grasshoppers and crickets, but also mantids, katydids, stick insects, soft arthropod larvae, pupae, egg cases, caterpillars, beetles, spiders and skinks. Large grasshoppers are usually stripped of their wings, legs, and often the head, before being fed to nestlings. Females give a low, soft repeated *grrk* note that stimulates nestlings to beg. As observed in all bowerbirds to date, the female parent takes faecal sacs from their younger nestlings. Females will chase other Spotted Bowerbirds and other birds from their nest and adjacent trees, often mimicking potential predators such as Whistling Kites and Blue-winged Kookaburras. If a potential predator of nestlings, such as a kookaburra, approaches a nest the female parent adopts a frozen posture until the predator departs. A female with nestlings will perform distraction displays and give vocal mimicry, and occasionally drop to the ground to creep through vegetation with a crippled-looking gait and neck stretched, feathers ruffled, and wings spread. On excessively hot days a female will protect her eggs or nestlings by sitting up and partly spreading her wings to provide shade.

Status and conservation

Numbers of birds sometimes attack fruit and vegetable gardens and are often killed for doing so. This bowerbird is considered extinct in South Australia, where it only ever had a small range, and remains a declining one in south New South Wales and Victoria. It is considered all but extinct and endangered in the latter State. Reasons for declines are thought to include illegal shooting and poisoning, predation by domestic and feral cats and Red Foxes, and widespread clearing and modification and fragmentation of habitat.

WESTERN BOWERBIRD
Chlamydera guttata
Etymology: *guttata* L. *guttatus,* speckled or spotted.

This bowerbird occurs in Western Australia from the North West Cape through the Pilbara and south into the central interior of that State, thence eastward in a narrowing band toward and across the Northern Territory border into the south of that State to about 200 to 300 kilometres north and east of Alice Springs, and extending to some 100 kilometres south of the Northern Territory and South Australia border and east to level with Alice Springs. Occurs at sea level to about 500 metres or more above it.

Description

A small, relatively short-tailed, richly coloured, bowerbird of the dry Australian interior that associates with rock-dwelling figs over much of its range. This species includes two geographical forms, or subspecies; see page 291.

28 cm. A medium-sized species of grey bowerbird, much like the Spotted Bowerbird in general appearance but with darker and richer colouring throughout and with underparts of a deeper and richer buff. The sexes are alike, but femlaes have no nape crest or a smaller one than do adult males; adult males and females are similar in size, although females have on average a slighter longer tail. For pictures of this bowerbird elsewhere see page 134.

Ecology and habits

Western Bowerbirds live mainly in riverine woodland but also in scrub thickets in rocky range, gorge, and break-away areas with available water, where Rock Figs are important to its diet. Typically inhabits dryer areas than Great Bowerbirds, some receiving as little as 13 centimetres of rain annually. Vagrancy occurs under drought conditions. A population about a clay pan deserted it, and an incompleted nest, as the last water evaporated. Birds are shy except in drought

Illustration of Western Bowerbirds, adult male above and female below, from Gould's *The Birds of Australia* Supplement of 1869 (opposite).

conditions, when thirst makes them bold. At well used campsites birds will come within metres of people for food and water, while remaining alert and ready to flee. Several birds will drink at waterholes, particularly during the hotter part of the day to the evening. Flight is direct at no great height above ground, rapid but laboured, and conspicuously undulating.

The vocal repertoire is similar to that of Spotted Bowerbirds, including vocal avian and other mimicry. Mimicry of some 13 bird species has been reported to have been given by several bower-owning males when potential predators were nearby, as well as human coughing, dog barking, cat meowing and horse whinnying. Females also mimic predators' calls at their nest. A Collared Sparrowhawk took a male at his bower.

This bird eats fruits, animals, flowers, buds, nectar, and seeds. The year-round availability of Rock Figs makes them an important part of the diet in some

An adult male Western Bowerbird in his bower avenue, Ormiston Gorge, Northern Territory.

areas but other fruits, including those of mistletoe, are also eaten. Animal foods include moths, beetles, grasshoppers, ants, and spiders. Birds are sufficiently adaptable to take advantage of unusual foods at garden feeders, camps and mobile home sites.

Bowers and courtship

Reproduces polygynously, the promiscuous males building and decorating avenue bowers. Traditional bowers are some two kilometres apart, some are less distant, depending upon availability of suitable bushes for them to be built beneath. Preferred bower sites have low overhanging foliaged branches of Rock Figs or other vegetation that provide concealment. Bower sites are said to never be far from water.

An adult male Western Bowerbird applying paint to the wall of his avenue bower, Ormiston Gorge, Northern Territory.

Bowers are similar to those of the Spotted Bowerbird. Four bowers on the Hamersley-Barlee Range of the Northern Territory averaged 36 centimetres long and 16 wide externally, with the avenue 23 high and their platform extending 48 beyond the end of the bower walls. The avenue is said to be orientated in no particular direction. Bower decorations include bones, snail shells, pebbles, calcite crystals, green fruits, buds, seedpods, glass, and brass ammunition cartridge cases and shotgun cartridge bases. Males paint their inner bower walls, one at Ormiston Gorge doing so intensively and extensively by using fruit pulp of a red-flowered emu-bush.

Males attend bowers most of the year but peak display occurs during August to December. New bowers are built at the same site as the previous one, with several disused bowers often within a metre of an active structure, or are re-located closeby. Bowers may be visited by groups of three to seven crestless younger birds. Extensive bower damage is inflicted upon bowers by visiting rival adult males and decoration theft, while unrecorded, probably occurs.

Courtship is little known: A male often responds to a visitor of his kind by adopting aggressive-like postures, and preventing it from approaching to within a metre of the bower. Courting males perform upward jumping with wing opening and flicking and other postures and movements similar to those of Spotted and Regent Bowerbirds. These include charging with head and bill held high, single and double wing flicks, head turning to present the nape accompanied by the partly fanned tailed being pulled sideways and forward toward the beak, and head shaking with a decoration held in the beak. Up to six birds will watch an adult male displaying at his bower, but successful courtship has only been observed in the absence of birds other than the female.

Breeding

Breeding takes place during July to March across the range of the species, being noted on the North West Cape in August to September with nestlings and fledglings during September to October. Eggs found in nests from July to December. Nests are mostly built in a low tree or bush, but occasionally in a vine tangle, or mistletoe, at two to six and an average of three metres above ground. The nest is a loose shallow bowl foundation, or a more firmly constructed neat one, of dead twigs and dry vine tendrils with a shallow eggcup lining of finer twigs, tendrils, casuarina needles, acacia phyllodes, and/or dried grass stems. Eggs are similar to those of Spotted Bowerbirds, but their ground colour is possibly slightly less greenish; 15 eggs average 38 x 25 millimetres. Only a few egg clutches are known with most being of two eggs; incubation and nestling periods, nestling care and development, and productivity remain unknown.

Status and conservation

Many birds were, and in remote places doubtless still are, killed as they attack garden fruits and vegetables. Western Bowerbirds were last recorded in the

WESTERN BOWERBIRD

South Australia Range region near Swan Reach in 1929. The North West Cape population, which constitutes the distinct form or subspecies *C. g. carteri*, was recently estimated to be stable at about 2000 breeding birds, occupying some 500 square kilometres, and was therefore classified as 'near threatened'.

An adult male Western Bowerbird courts another individual in his bower, Ormiston Gorge, Northern Territory.

GREAT BOWERBIRD

Chlamydera nuchalis
Etymology: *nuchalis* Mod. L. nuchal or of the nape [crest].

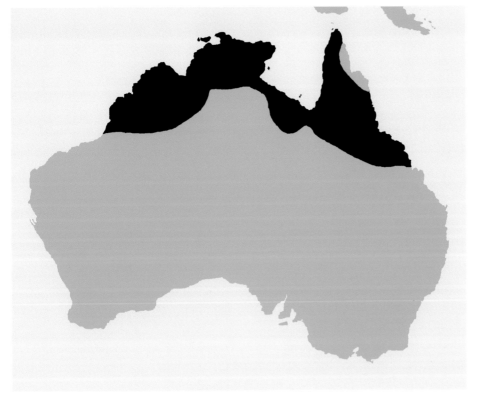

Birds occupy most of the Australian tropics north of 20 degrees south, that is the Kimberley Division, Northern Territory, north Queensland, and offshore islands, to just south of 20 degrees south in mid and east Queensland. Absent from the humid coastal area of Cardwell north to Tully and the eastern watershed of the Wet Tropics ranges, but present on Cape Melville and northward to Cape York, Queensland. At sea level to about 600 metres or more above it. Birds live with Spotted Bowerbirds at about 100 kilometres south-southeast of Charters Towers, where their favoured habitats abut and hybridization occurs rarely.

Description

A large, pale, relative slender, large-billed, long-necked, vocal widespread bowerbird of tropical Australia. This species includes two geographical forms, or subspecies; see page 291.

35 cm. The largest species of grey bowerbird, that is entirely a drab grey that is slightly darker and greyer on the chin, throat, upper chest and on the upperparts. The crown is variably finely spotted with a darker and a silvery colour and the nape is decorated with an erectile filamentous pinkish crest. The darker plumage of the back, wings, and tail are conspicuously spotted with large pale, whitish, tips to the mantle, back, and flight feathers. Bill blackish, eye dark brown; legs olive-brown. The sexes are alike, but femlaes have no crest or a smaller one than do adult males; adult males are larger than females, notably in wing length and weight. For pictures of this bowerbird elsewhere see pages 13, 82, 86, 89, 97, 102, 104, 105, 143, 147, 272.

Ecology and habits

Great Bowerbirds frequent eucalypt forests and woodlands, particularly riverine forest and thicket within it, mangroves and rain- and monsoon-forest edges,

Illustration of Great Bowerbirds, adult male in foreground and female behind, from Sharpe's *Monograph of the Paradiseidae and Ptilonorhynchidae* of 1891-1898 (opposite).

suburbs and gardens. They are usually close to water, but will also breed in near waterless habitat. Birds are animated, curious, and fond of bathing. Flight over distance is swift, direct, and undulating, with wing feather tips curled upward under the pressure of down strokes. Their colouration and markings make them cryptic in the dappled light of bower sites. Birds are rarely seen in numbers away from bowers, save odd aggregations of up to 20 to 30 occasionally gathering in a single fruiting tree to feed.

The vocal repertoire of males includes loud harsh bower advertisement song notes, explosive hissings, churrings, cacklings, and chatterings, vocal avian and other mimicry including numerous sounds of human activity, machines and voices, cat-like calls and dog barking. Mimicry of the calls of predatory birds is commonly performed by males at their bowers, and by females at their nests, when approached by people. Collared Sparrowhawks, Red Goshawks, and pythons have predated Great Bowerbirds.

Fruits, including those of figs and cultivated exotic plants, flowers, nectar, seeds, green vegetables, and animals are eaten. Toxic fruits of the exotic Cookbush, under which bowers are also sited, are eaten. Males cache fruit in forks of branches above their bower for later consumption. Birds boldly frequent bird feeders. Animal foods include grasshoppers, beetles including weevils, plant bugs, ants, lepidopteran caterpillars and pupae, and larvae of other insects and spiders. Birds will eat bread and other camp scraps.

Bowers and courtship

Reproduces polygynously, the promiscuous males building and decorating substantial stick avenue bowers. Traditional bower sites are typically a few metres into, or close to the edge of, riverine or other protective vegetation immediately adjacent to expansive open habitat. Often they are close to permanent water but not invariably. Some are even sited just above high water line beneath beach crest vegetation or mangroves and, rarely, within mangroves that are flooded by exceptional tides. Traditional bower sites are one to two kilometres apart, but this depends upon the availability of suitable protective bushes under which bowers are built. Preferred sites have a canopy of a low shading and concealing thicket, shrub, or tree. Bowers are commonly built in parks, gardens, on quieter footpaths, and even within or, if overhung by foliage, atop buildings. Traditional bower sites persist on the same spot for in excess of five decades. Younger males frequent rudimentary bower sites close to the traditional bower of an adult male, for several weeks to several months. They may gather at rudimentary 'bowers' that consist of no more than a tree trunk base, a mat of sticks on the ground, or a poorly constructed avenue, with few if any decorations. Immature males also attend bowers of adult males, in their absence, particularly before and after the peak of the display season.

Bowers of adult males are long, substantial, thick-walled avenues of stout sticks; the tops of the inwardly-curving central inner wall sticks sometimes meeting, to form a tunnel. The stick platform, upon which the avenue is built, is substantial and the floor at either avenue entrance often raised above both the platform and the central floor of the avenue. Odd bowers, with additional walls, are known. A particularly unusual Great Bowerbird's bower that we examined in Townsville City consisted of a much-shortened avenue encircled at one side by two walls. These additional two walls would have formed a complete semi-circle if it were not for a gap left in the middle. Fifty-four bowers at Townsville, Queensland, averaged 61 centimetres long, 51 wide, and 37 high externally, with the avenue 14 wide. Ten bowers along the McCleod River, Queensland, averaged 51 centimetres wide and 37 long externally, with the avenue 59 long and 15 wide, and the exposed length of the platform averaging 57 centimetres.

An unusual Great Bowerbird's bower viewed from above with two semi-circular walls, at top of picture, additional to the the usual avenue, Townsville, Queensland.

Sticks in only one wall of bowers numbered 700 to 920, males carrying a total of some 4000 to 5000 twigs to their bower site, one to four at a time. The avenue is typically orientated across the path of the sun's trajectory, to be at or close to a north-south alignment, but with some variation between localities.

Bower decorations are numerous, and are variable in and between any given area. Almost universally included, however, are land-snail shells, mammal bones, some green fruits and/or leaves, and some red or reddish items. Decorations numbers on a bower site vary from some hundreds up to 12,000, the majority of them being white and grey. They are laid on the court, only rarely in or atop the avenue walls. In the odd bower fine twiglets are placed horizontally along the top of the avenue walls. Innumerable human-made objects are often used: for example within Townsville City a bower in a cemetery was decorated with marble chips and artificial flowers taken from graves; a university campus bower with pens, paper clips, and other stationary; one within an army barracks with spent firearm cartridges and other accoutrements; another beside a council workshop was decorated with green plastic hinge-pins for garbage bins. Near coasts marine mollusc shells and pieces of bleached coral are used. Birds enter homes in search of food and stories about the loss of jewellery, keys, and such like, and in some cases the subsequent retrieval of them from a bower, abound. Males commonly paint their inner bower walls, and this behaviour involves much time and leaves a conspicuous brown stain on walls.

The display season extends from May or June to December or early January, but commences as early as February at some localities. Bowers may be built each season or a structure used over consecutive years. New bowers are erected under the same bush as the previous one or beneath another bush nearby, up to about 100 metres distant, but within the same bower site. Several derelict stuctures from previous seasons might remain under bushes of the bower site. One active Townsville bower had eight old ones beneath the same bush, three more beneath an adjacent one and another beneath another smaller bush, all within a 25 metre radius.

Males attend their bower site for more than 50% of daylight, where they

An adult male Great Bowerbird presents a clothes peg, the same colour as his crest, to a female within his bower, Townsville Queensland.

GREAT BOWERBIRD

An adult male Great Bowerbird in the strutting run of his peripheral courtship display, Charters Towers, Queensland.

give advertisement vocalisations, maintain bowers, display and chase away conspecifics or are just silent. Advertisement vocalisations are given from regularly used perches at the tops of six to eight metre tall trees averaging 30 to 200 metres from bowers, during the peak display season males singing closer to their bowers. Males take some three weeks to complete a rough bower at the start of a season, while a male can replace a damaged bower in two and a half days or less. Rival adult males damage bowers and steal decorations from each other. This bowerbird's plumage makes it highly cryptic in shady bowers locations, as with all other grey bowerbirds.

In an area where both bower-attending Great and Spotted Bowerbirds occur each species visits the adjacent bowers of the other. When one adult male Great displays to another of his own kind one or more Spotteds show intense interest by standing nearby and watching closely. Moreover, a Spotted will occasionally join a courting Great in his peripheral displays. The only time a male Great appears to resent the presence of a Spotted is as he displays to a female of his kind, when he will chase the latter off between displays.

Like the courtship of Spotteds, the displays of Greats are separable into central and peripheral ones. During central displays an *Upright* posture involves the male facing the female and drawing himself upright with sleeked plumage and beak open. As he calls his tongue is frequently flicked out. He high-steps forward and may hold a decoration in his beak. This frequently leads to a *Forward stretch* posture in which he faces the female, his feathers usually sleeked but sometimes ruffled, neck outstretched, snake-like, and head often turned to one side, sometimes held low and strained forward. His crest is often only slightly expanded and a decoration tossed to one side while this posture is held. By rotating his head sideways and downward he then often proceeds to a nape presentation posture. With his beak lowered and head turned so that his crest is directed towards the female, his wings drooped and tail raised. If standing to the left of his bower avenue entrance he turns his head to the left, and *vice versa.* He then jerks his head abruptly, accompanied by a ticking sound. Meanwhile, his crest may be partly to fully open. His body feathers are sleeked or ruffled.

Before, during, and/or after the forward-stretching and crest presentation postures the male will touch, grasp, or probe the sticks at the end of a bower wall, to shake or nudge that part of the structure gently. While the female cannot see the male during this behaviour she can see the movement of the bower wall. Over time this behaviour creates a neat indentation at the point on the end of the bower wall.

During peripheral displays the male circles his bower in a strutting walk. He sometimes sleeks his plumage, with wings raised and tail horizontal, but more often his body feathers are ruffled with wings drooped, sometimes partly spread, to almost touch the ground. His tail is cocked up and his crest fully expanded. A decoration is often held in the bill and as he parades around he produces loud hisses and ticks. His attitudes become lopsided at times as he tilts wings and tail slightly in her direction. When he becomes intensely excited he circles his bower in a hopping version of the peripheral display. There is no rigid sequence in which these various postures and movements appear, and peripheral runs might be preceded or followed by displays of the central type. The discrete postures and

A courting adult male Great Bowerbird directs his nape presentation display toward his bower avenue, from where his audience watches, Townsville, Queensland.

movements are separated by a variety of jumps and sidestepping movements. Mating takes place within, sometimes immediately outside, the avenue.

Breeding

Breeding is known during most months, save April and June, across the species range: egg laying peaking during October to November. Nestlings are present during October to March, with fledged young being fed by parents in February, March, and April. A female was seen foraging on fruit with her identical-looking dependant young in March. Nests are mostly built in trees, bushes and saplings, but sometimes in mistletoe clumps, pandanus fronds, and vine tangles, some two to nine and at an average of five, metres above ground. Repeated use of a nest site or tree is not unusual. One successful nest was located 50 metres from an active bower site of more than 10 years standing. Six nests averaged 64 metres from the closest active bower.

Nests are loosely built, shallow to deep, saucers with a foundation of slender sticks and twigs with an eggcup lining of finer twigs and a few leaves. The egg ground colour is as Spotted Bowerbirds or is, perhaps more often, less greenish and more creamy to buff; 264 eggs average 41 x 29 millimetres. One to two, rarely three, eggs are laid but 72% of 234 clutches were of one egg. Two eggs in one nest we studied hatched a day apart and incubation lasted 21 days and the nestling period 20 to 21 days. Brooding ceases when nestlings are 14 to 15 days old, irrespective of brood size.

Nestlings are fed slightly more animals than fruit. Figs are a major component, representing more than 40%, of the fruit diet. More than half of animal foods fed to nestlings are grasshoppers, almost all being stripped of their head, legs, and wings before being fed to the nestlings. Other animals include crickets, katydids, mantids, caterpillars, beetles, moths, flies, cockroaches and skinks. The female parent removes the faeces of younger nestlings. Mimicry of calls of predatory birds is commonly performed by nesting females when approached by people, and females at nests will mimic cat meowing and dog barking. Females will also perform a distraction display, by hopping about the ground with tightly sleeked plumage and drooped wings while giving vocal mimicry of potential predator calls. Females will chase other Great Bowerbirds from trees adjacent to their nest tree.

Status and conservation

Common where extensive appropriate habitat exists and, if permitted, will associate closely with humans. Interestingly Great Bowerbirds and their bowers are more numerous about a mining town than in undisturbed habitat, presumably due to water, food, and shelter access, on Koolan Island. The species appears to have declined in the southern Atherton Tableland area of north Queensland since 1940. Birds, particularly in winter flocks of 30 or more, attack soft fruit and green vegetable crops and are not uncommonly killed as a result in remote locations.

This Carpet Python contains the Great Bowerbird that used to attend this bower, Townsville, Queensland. By and courtesy of Marnie McCullough (over page).

APPENDIX

The species and subspecies of bowerbirds[1]

White-eared Catbird
Ailuroedus buccoides
   Ailuroedus buccoides buccoides
   Ailuroedus buccoides cinnamomeus
   Ailuroedus buccoides geislerorum
   Ailuroedus buccoides stonii
Black-eared Catbird
Ailuroedus melanotis
   Ailuroedus melanotis melanotis
   Ailuroedus melanotis arfakianus
   Ailuroedus melanotis astigmaticus
   Ailuroedus melanotis facialis
   Ailuroedus melanotis guttaticollis
   Ailuroedus melanotis joanae
   Ailuroedus melanotis jobiensis
   Ailuroedus melanotis maculosus
   Ailuroedus melanotis melanocephalus
   Ailuroedus melanotis misoliensis
Green Catbird
Ailuroedus crassirostris
Tooth-billed Bowerbird
Scenopoeetes dentirostris
Macgregor's Bowerbird
Amblyornis macgregoriae
   Amblyornis macgregoriae macgregoriae
   Amblyornis macgregoriae amati
   Amblyornis macgregoriae germanus
   Amblyornis macgregoriae kombok
   Amblyornis macgregoriae lecroyae
   Amblyornis macgregoriae mayeri
   Amblyornis macgregoriae nubicola
Streaked Bowerbird
Amblyornis subalaris
Vogelkop Bowerbird
Amblyornis nornatus

Yellow-fronted Bowerbird
Amblyornis flavifrons
Archbold's Bowerbird
Archboldia papuensis
   Archboldia papuensis papuensis
   Archboldia papuensis sanfordi
Golden Bowerbird
Prionodura newtoniana
Masked Bowerbird
Sericulus aureus
Flame Bowerbird
Sericulus ardens
Adelbert Bowerbird
Sericulus bakeri
Regent Bowerbird
Sericulus chrysocephalus
Satin Bowerbird
Ptilonorhynchus violaceus
   Ptilonorhynchus violaceus violaceus
   Ptilonorhynchus violaceus minor
Lauterbach's Bowerbird
Chlamydera lauterbachi
   Chlamydera lauterbachi lauterbachi
   Chlamydera lauterbachi uniformis
Fawn-breasted Bowerbird
Chlamydera cerviniventris
Spotted Bowerbird
Chlamydera maculata
Western Bowerbird
Chlamydera guttata
   Chlamydera guttata guttata
   Chlamydera guttata carteri
Great Bowerbird
Chlamydera nuchalis
   Chlamydera nuchalis nuchalis
   Chlamydera nuchalis orientalis

[1] Author and full publication details of each description and subspecies distributions appear in our 2004 book (see *Further reading*). Species names are in **boldface** and subspecies are not.

EPILOGUE

The reader is now holding a comprehensive summary of all that is known about the history of discovery and the lives and works of all of the living bowerbirds. As birds go there can be no doubt that bowerbirds richly deserve the application to them of adjectives such as amazing, wonderful or, indeed, incredible. We described in our *Prologue* the thrill of being the first ornithologists to witness what appears to be the complete courtship display of Golden Bowerbirds. At close quarters we watched and heard an adult male hide from the female of his wooing attentions while seeking to impress her with his learning ability, memory, and skill in mimicking the calls of many other birds. But this was only one of many novel discoveries we were fortunate enough to make during our many months and years spent in museums and bowerbird habitats respectively.

In museums we were able to examine and measure two and a half thousand stuffed bowerbird study skins held in 32 collections around the world. This enabled us to assess and discuss the validity of all described bowerbird species and forms, or subspecies, and to quantitatively and qualitatively define differences between the sexes and various age classes of the 20 different bowerbirds. As a result we published a string of papers in the scientific literature dealing with various taxonomic problems. These are synthesised and detailed in our 2004 academic book (see Further reading). A visit to the Bernice Bishop Museum in Hawaii resulted in the surprise discovery of a completely new and distinctive form of Macgregor's Bowerbird, which we named *Amblyornis macgregriae lecroyae* after our ornitholgical colleage and friend Mrs Mary LeCroy of the American Museum of Natural History in New York. In New York and also in the Papua New Guinea Museum, Port Moresby, we discovered specimens that indicate the, previously unsuspected, hybridisation between the Streaked and Macgregor's Bowerbirds.

But it is our discoveries concerning living bowerbirds that most satisfy and please us, particularly as next to nothing was known about some of the species that are now, as a result of our studies, among the best known of bowerbirds. Firstly, we confirmed that only one parent Tooth-bill, the female, attends the nest - contrary to previous statements in the literature. Whether or not the Tooth-billed Bowerbird could mimic the calls of other birds was also long hotly debated and we, together with our friend and neighbour Mike McGuire, were able to prove conclusively that it does so – extremely well and often. Another finding concerning the Tooth-billed Bowerbird was that its beak is far more sophisticatedly 'toothed' than was previously appreciated. Its toothed beak was thought to be for plucking leaves for court decoration by males, but we showed that this is actually an adaptation to the predominantly leaf-eating winter diet of birds - of both sexes and all ages. This enables the birds to crush and masticate leaf matter before ingesting it, thus enhancing digestion of this unusual diet.

While the Spotted and Great Bowerbirds had never been found to

An adult male Golden Bowerbird returns to his massive bower structure with another piece of beard lichen to add to his accumulated bower decorations.

occur together we strongly suspected that they must do so somewhere and by systematically searching we not only found such co-existence but also found that they sometimes hybridise. We even found ourselves able to photograph an adult male Great Bowerbird courting a hybrid Great-cross-Spotted individual in his bower as a male Spotted Bowerbird looked on (see page 272)! Also we were lucky enough to come across accessible active nests of the Spotted and Great Bowerbirds and as a result were able to describe their nesting biology for the first time. Having closely observed females egg laying at numbers of nests of several species we could confirm that bowerbirds, unusually, lay the eggs of their clutches on alternate days. Most songbirds lay eggs on consecutive days. In upland New Guinea grasslands we systematically watched, photographed, and described male Fawn-breasted and Lauterbach's Bowerbirds courting at their bowers and females of them caring for their eggs and nestlings; the latter for the first time.

We heard that Archbold's Bowerbird had been sighted at some 2500 to 2800 metres above sea level in the Tari Gap of the Southern Highlands, Papua New Guinea, where it was previously unknown. So we made our way to this cold and wet place and spent two exhausting months clambering through moss forest until we found our first bower. Once we had seen this bower and the kind of situation it had been built in we were able to locate some 20 more in the following season and study the birds' behaviour. With the aid of a video camera we were able to describe the courtship and mating of Archbold's Bowerbird.

Our single most surprising and exciting discovery is that adult male Archbold's Bowerbirds specifically decorate their bowers with the head plumes of adult male King of Saxony Birds of Paradise. They do this solely to impress their females (see Chapters 3 and 6). We found between one and six of these plumes only on each of the six largest of the 24 bowers that we studied. As male King of Saxony Birds of Paradise very likely do not acquire adult plumage until at least six to seven years old and then wear only two head plumes one can appreciate how rare a bower decoration these feathers represent. Presumably males with numbers of these feathers on their bower would have greater chances of successful courtships. The inevitable question is then, what would a male Archbold's Bowerbird response be to a fully-plumaged male King of Saxony Bird of Paradise perching beside him? Who knows? After countless hours of exhaustive searching over several seasons we were particularly delighted to be the first to discover and describe the nest and egg of Archbold's Bowerbird, in 1988. By building a tower of small tree trunks we were able to sit in a blind of fern fronds to watch and photograph the nesting biology of this, almost mystical, New Guinea highland bowerbird in intimate detail.

But our most substantial original bowerbird findings undoubtedly result from our intensive long-term studies of pairs of Black-eared Catbirds at their nests and over their home ranges, of male Tooth-billed Bowerbirds at their courts and home ranges, and of every aspect of male Golden Bowerbirds at bowers, females at nests, and both sexes in their habitat. These studies effectively took us from knowledge limited to the nest, nest site and eggs of the three species to a comprehensive appreciation of their entire biology. In addition to these intensive long term studies of bowerbirds, similar such studies of the birds of paradise in both New Guinea and Australia resulted in Clifford being awarded a doctorate for his scientific publication-based thesis on bowerbirds and birds of paradise.

The bowerbirds have long attracted a great deal of scientific and popular attention. This should not, however, lead to the assumption that we know a great deal about them. Because what bowerbirds do, often in the world's most inaccessible and uncomfortable forests, is so much more complex and intriguing than what most other birds do they inevitably require intense and long term investigation. There remains much to learn, examine, and test.

The scientific community knows precious little about some half of the 20 known bowerbird species. It is also true that we cannot be absolutely sure that some unknown bowerbird species does not await discovery on a remote New Guinea mountain. After all, Archbold's Bowerbird (now known to be widely, if patchily, distributed over the New Guinea highlands) was not made known to science until as recently as 1940, and we did not discover its nests and eggs until 1988. The home of the Yellow-fronted Bowerbird was not discovered, or a live bird seen by any scientist, until 1979; and the bower of the Adelbert Bowerbird was not known until 1986. The nest and eggs of the latter two species remain undiscovered, as do those of the Masked and Flame Bowerbirds. What have now become easily accessible Australian species, such as the Fawn-breasted, Western and Great Bowerbirds, have still received little close attention, while the wet forests of New Guinea house a veritable treasure trove of bowerbird biology awaiting observation, description, experimentation, and interpretation.

To ornithologists, days such as we experienced in the field in making the above findings are the stuff of dreams. The most important result of our work is, however, that we now love, admire, and wish to protect the bowerbirds more than ever. As life on our planet suffers increasing pressure from the human hoards the passion of knowledgeable naturalists becomes every bit as important as that of academics in the struggle for conservation: A struggle that must in large measure be supported through public awareness and appreciation.

"This extraordinary family of avian architects and artists can surely tell us something of the origin of aesthetics; that any of them should become extinct through human neglect is surely unthinkable."

[From Diamond et al. *Save the Birds*, see Further reading.]

ACKNOWLEDGEMENTS

As our recent academic book contains acknowledgment of the generous people that kindly helped with its preparation we do not repeat them all here. We would, however, thank the following for making unpublished facts available to us or for permitting us to reproduce their photographs herein, as credited: Bruce Beehler, Brett Benz, Will Betz, Dan Blunt, Brian Coates, Adrian Forsyth, R.F. Haselgrove of Mildara Wines, Simon B. Jensen, Roy Mackay, Mary Jo McConnell, Simon Nevill, Mike Potts, Steve Richards, Ian Rowley, D. Schuelein, William (Bill) Thomas, Glen Threlfo, Nancy Woodman. All photographs not attributed by name to others are the work of C. B. Frith. We acknowledge kind permission to reproduce images in the care of the Natural History Museum, London; Mitchell Library, Sydney; Queensland Museum, Brisbane; National Library of Australia, Canberra, Cairns Historical Society, and the Australian Postal Corporation, as detailed in picture captions herein. It is not always possible to establish copyright ownership and, therefore, anyone who feels their rights have been infringed is welcome to contact the publishers.

Other friends and colleagues that have helped us in various ways include Joan Airey, David Attenborough, Bob and Pam Bates of Trans Niugini Tours, Joe Benshemesh, Will Betz, David Bishop, Dan Blunt, Stanley and Kaisa Breeden, Kathy Buckley, Terry Carmichael, Brian Coates, Gabriel Crowley, Ann Datta, Richard Donaghey, Johannes Erritzoe, Stephen Garnett, Derek Goodwin, Andree Griffin, Martin Grossetti, Colin Harrison, Darryl Jones, Mary LeCroy, Alan Lill, Wayne Longmore, Randall and Catherine Machejefski, Roy Mackay, Joah Madden, Paul Maxwell, Mary Jo McConnell, Marnie McCullough and her wonderful family Bob, Annette, Brian and Amanda, Mike McGuire, Kate Mobbs, Jamie Owen, Thane Pratt, Tim Robson, Ian Rowley, Eleanor Russell, David Snow, Andrew Taplin, Al Uy and Kathie Way. We thank Stanley Breeden for helpfully commenting upon drafts of chapters 1 to 6, while responsibility for all herein remains entirely ours. We are especially grateful to our good friends Stan and Kaisa Breeden for digital image preparation advise and support, to Kaisa for her exceptional colour management expertise, and Randall Machejefski for kindly and generously preparing the fine computer generated distribution maps. We acknowledge our dept to the admirable bowerbird ecology and nesting biology studies of Norman Chaffer, Jared Diamond, Richard Donaghey, Tom Gilliard, Gary Innis, Norbert Lenz, Joah Madden, Jock Marshall, Paul Maxwell, Jim McEvoy, Stephen and Melinda Pruett-Jones, Tim Robson, Rita and Sid Vellenga, and John Warham. Inspiration for the design of this book was derived in part from Errol Fuller's splendid *Extinct Birds* (O.U.P., 2000).

Warwick Forge, of Bloomings Books and Luke Harris, of Chameleon Print Design, Melbourne, provided invaluable professional expertise.

We most gratefully acknowledge the financial support of the Norman Wettenhall Foundation, all committee members and staff, which was critical in seeing this book into print. This book is dedicated to the memory of Norman Wettenhall, who did so much for Australasian ornithology.

FURTHER READING

Becarri, O. 1878. The gardener bird and a new orchid. *Gardener's Chronical* 16: 332.

Bell, H.L. The Flamed Bowerbird, *Sericulus aureus*. *Emu* 70: 64-68.

Blunt, D. and Frith, C.B. 2005. A living 'Rawnsley's Bowerbird – an adult male resulting from a hybridisation in the wild between a Regent *Sericulus chrysocephalus* and a Satin *Ptilonorhynchus violaceus* Bowerbird. *Australian Field Ornithology* 22: 53-57.

Borgia, G. 1995. Why do bowerbirds build bowers? *American Scientist* 83: 542-547.

Breeden, S. and Wright, B. 1989. *Kakadu: looking after the country – the Gagudju way.* Simon and Schuster, Sydney.

Campbell, A.J. 1901. *Nests and Eggs of Australian Birds.* Pawson and Brailsford, Sheffield.

Chaffer, N. 1984. *In Quest of Bowerbirds.* Rigby, Adelaide.

Coates, B.J. 1990. *Birds of Papua New Guinea, Volume 2.* Dove Publications, Brisbane.

Cooper, W.T. and Forshaw, J.M. 1977. *The Birds of Paradise and Bower Birds.* Collins. Sydney.

Diamond, A.W., Schreiber, R.L., Attenborough, D., and Prestt, I. 1987. *Save the Birds.* Cambridge University Press, Cambridge.

Diamond, J.M. 1982. Evolution of bowerbirds, animal origins of the aesthetic sense. *Nature,* 297: 99-102.

Diamond. J.M. 1986. Animal art, variation in bower decorating style among male bowerbirds *Amblyornis inornatus. Proceedings of the National Academy of Science,* 83: 3042-6.

Donaghey, R.H. 1996. *Bowerbirds.* Pp. 138-187 in Strahan, R. (editor), *Finches, bowerbirds & other Passerines of Australia.* Angus & Robertson, Sydney.

Dwyer, P., Minnegal, M., and Thomson, J. 1985. Odds and ends, Bower birds as taphonomic agents. *Australian Archaeology* 21: 1-10.

Edwards, G. 1750. *A Natural History of Birds,* volume 3. London.

Elliot, D.G. 1873. *A Monograph of the Paradisidae.* The Author, London.

Everett, M. 1978. *The Birds of Paradise and Bowerbirds.* Putnams, New York.

Frith, C.B. 2006. A history and reassessment of the unique but missing specimen of Rawnsley's Bowerbird *Ptilonorhynchus rawnsleyi,* Diggles 1867, (Aves: Ptilonorhynchidae). *Historical Biology* 18: 53-64.

Frith, C.B. and Beehler, B.M. 1998. *The Birds of Paradise – Paradisaeidae.* Oxford University Press, Oxford.

Frith, C.B. and Frith, D.W. 2004. *The Bowerbirds – Ptilonorhynchidae.* Oxford University Press, Oxford.

Garnett, S.T. and Crowley, G.M. 2000. *The Action Plan for Australian Birds* 2000. Environment Australia, Canberra.

Gilliard, E.T. 1969. *Birds of Paradise and Bower Birds.* Weidenfeld and Nicolson, London.

Gould, J. 1840-8. *The Birds of Australia, Volume 4*. The author, London.

Gould, J. 1841. On the "Run" or Playing-house constructed by the Satin Bird (*Ptilonorhynchus holosericeus*), and on a similar structure formed by the *Chlamydera maculata* of Australia. *Proceeedings of the Zoological Society of London*, 1841, Part 8 (April): 92-4.

Gould, J. and Sharpe, R.B. 1875-88. *The Birds of New Guinea and Adjacent Papuan Islands, Volume 1*. Sotheran, London.

Higgins, P.J., Peter, J.M. and Cowling, S.J. (editors) 2006. *Handbook of Australian, New Zealand and Antarctic Birds. Volume 7: Boatbill to Starlings*. Oxford University Press, Melbourne.

Iredale, T. 1950. *Birds of Paradise and Bowerbirds*. Georgian House, Melbourne.

Johnsgard, P.A. 1994. *Arena birds - sexual selection and behaviour*. Smithsonian Institution Press, Washington.

Johnstone, R.E. and Storr, G.M. 2004. *Handbook of Western Australian birds. Volume 2, Passerines*. Western Australian Museum, Perth.

Lenz, N. 1999. Evolutionary ecology of the Regent Bowerbird *Sericulus chrysocephalus. Okologie der Vogel* 22: Supplement 1-200.

Lesson, R.P. 1834-5. *Histoire Naturelle de Oiseaux dev Paradis et dev Epimaques*. Arthus Bertrand, Paris.

Le Vaillant, F. 1801-6. *Histoire naturelle des oiseaux de paradis et des rolliers*. Chez   Denne le jeune [et] Perlet, Paris.

Lewin, J.W. 1808. *Birds of New Holland*. White and Bagster, London.

Linneaus, C. 1758. *Systema Naturaeper Regna Tria Naturae*. 1. Laurentii Salvii, Stockholm.

Lumholtz, C. 1889. *Among cannibals*. Murray, London.

Madden, J. 2001. Sex, bowers and brains. *Proceedings of the Royal Society of London* B, 268: 833-8.

Majnep, I.S. and Bulmer, R. 1977. *Birds of My Kalem Country*. Auckland University Press, Auckland.

Marshall, A.J. 1954. *Bower-birds, their Displays and Breeding Cycles - a preliminary statement*. Oxford University Press, Oxford.

Mathews, G.M. 1925-7. *The Birds of Australia, Volume 12*. The author, London.

North, A.J. 1901-14. *Nests and eggs of birds found breeding in Australia and Tasmania*. Special Catalogue, No. 1, Australian Museum, Sydney.

Pruett-Jones, M. and Pruett-Jones, S. 1983. The bowerbird's labour of love. *Natural History* 9: 49-55.

Schodde, R and Mason, I.J. 1999. *The directory of Australian birds, Passerines*. CSIRO, Melbourne.

Sharpe, R.B. 1891-8. *Monograph of the Paradisaeidae, or Birds of Paradise, and Ptilonorhynchidae, or Bower-birds*. Parts 1-8. H. Sotheran and Co., London.

Sorenson, E. S. *Spotty, the Bower Bird and other nature stories*. Whitcombe & Tombs, Melbourne.

Swadling, P. 1996. *Plumes from Paradise*. Papua New Guinea National Musum, Port Moresby and Robert Brown, Brisbane.

Uy, J.A.C. 2002. Say it with bowers. *Natural History* 111: 78-82.

GENERAL INDEX

Page numbers for main accounts and illustrations of the bowerbird species are denoted by **bold type**. Other illustrations are denoted by numbers in *italics*. Plural numbers in normal type indicate pages dealing with a subject(s) at length. Each bowerbird species can be located by its English name (e.g. Black-eared Catbird or Catbird, Black-eared), genus (e.g. *Ailuroedus melanotis*), or its specific name (e.g. *melanotis, Ailuroedus*). Geographical localities, animal and plant names, and alternative scientific and common names for bowerbirds, are not included herein. Subspecies names are not indexed – these all appear in the table that is the Appendix.

GREYSCALE

BIN TRAVELER FORM

Cut By _M Murar_ Qty _20_ Date _07.15_

Scanned By _____ Qty _____ Date _____

Scanned Batch IDs

_____ _____ _____

Notes / Exception

_____

_____

_____

_____

_____